629.13   Becker, Beril 5794
BEC
        Dreams and
        realities of
        the conquest
        of the skies

DATE		
JAN 18		
JAN 25		
NOV 6		
MAY 6		
FEB 21 1997		

5794

Dreams and Realities
of the
Conquest of the Skies

Dreams and Realities
of the
Conquest of the Skies

Beril Becker

Atheneum   1968   New York

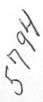

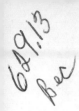

Copyright © 1967 by Beril Becker
All rights reserved
Library of Congress catalog card number 67-18991
Published simultaneously in Canada by
McClelland & Stewart Ltd.
Manufactured in the United States of America
Printed by Halliday Lithograph Corporation,
West Hanover, Massachusetts
Bound by H. Wolff, New York
Designed by David Rogers
First Printing September 1967
Second Printing August 1968

To Ruth

Contents

Dreams and Realities of the Conquest of the Skies

Early Theories of Flight

IN THE ANCIENT WORLD FLYING BELONGED TO THE GODS. THE sun god of Egypt, Ra, flew with falcon wings. Mercury had winged sandals. Apollo in a chariot pulled the sun across the sky.

But men, too, entered the legends of speculation. We hear of Daedalus, a Cretan engineer, who learned to fly. Is there an unknown history behind Daedalus and his son, Icarus? Daedalus was skillful enough to build one of the great engineering works of the ancient world, the famous Labyrinth of King Minos of Crete.

It is interesting to speculate that there might be a connection between the sudden collapse of Cretan civilization in 1400 B.C. and the mysterious flight of Daedalus and Icarus. Did they seek to escape in gliders from the violent earthquake and inundation that overwhelmed Crete? Icarus was supposed to have lost his life because the wax that held his wings was melted by the sun. Could it have been instead his glider that collapsed?

By 400 B.C. Greek technology had advanced to the point where intricate mechanical clocks and calendars were built.

3

In that period of history we hear of another flying wonder—the mechanical bird of Archytas of Tarantum, a Greek general and engineer. The records are lost, and we do not know whether this mechanical bird was sent flying by a clockwork mechanism or by use of jets of steam.

The history of flight begins again with a new civilization in the year 1256 A.D., when Roger Bacon published his *Mirror of Alchemy*. His scientific insights and predictions, like scattered seeds, grew and multiplied. Bacon suggested that the surface of the atmosphere must be a kind of "liquid fire" or "ethereal air." This first prophet of mechanical inventions projected two methods by which man would be able to fly through the air. If "ethereal air" were obtainable, it could be enclosed in thin copper spheres, making it possible to carry a man aloft as a cork rises in water. Or else it might be worthwhile for man to invent a flying instrument that could be made to flap wings, to reach in this way the treasure of "liquid fire." Thus, at the very dawn of the history of flight, we have lighter-than-air and heavier-than-air competing with each other in the scientific imagination of one man.

Leonardo Da Vinci, two centuries later, concentrated on a heavier-than-air machine. He wrote, "A bird is an instrument working in accordance with mathematical law; which instrument it is in the capacity of man to produce." He failed to get his ornithopter, a self-propelled device, to work with the muscle power of arms and legs. Had he persisted he might have created an aerodynamic glider, because he grasped the principles of air resistance and balanced flight. He seemed to see that when air flowed fast enough above and below a proper surface, lift occurred. This lift could keep a properly shaped object in the air for as long a time as the lift was present.

However, this supremely gifted genius, did go on to design a parachute—a starched linen dome eighteen feet square. Following his pattern, such a square parachute was built by a Venetian architect in 1618. Gripping the strings that dangled

A model of Leonardo da Vinci's heavier-than-air machine. *Smithsonian Institution.*

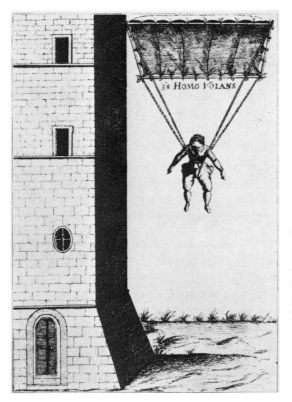

Square parachute constructed by Faust Veranzio, a Venetian architect, after a design by Leonardo da Vinci.

from each corner of his frame of rods, he managed to float down from high buildings, the first reported successful step in man's conquest of the air.

Since parachutes suggested the idea that air offered resistance, Galileo felt that air might be a substance that could be weighed. He blew extra air into a sealed vessel and found that the weight of the vessel increased. The fact that air could be contracted and expanded excited scientists in all the advanced countries. Inventors, taking their clue from water pumps, created various kinds of air pumps to study the weights and pressures of air.

These investigations intrigued the head of a German principality, Otto von Guericke, and he created a pump capable of leaving a more perfect vacuum within a sphere. Then came a historic demonstration. Von Guericke made a brass sphere with two hemispheres, whose flanged edges fitted exactly, and from which all the air had been pumped out. Not even twenty horses tugging at either end, could pull the hemispheres apart. It became clear that man was living at the bottom of a heavy gas that pressed down on everything. The invisible air had become a palpable ocean that might be navigated by vessels as were the seven seas.

Throughout the seventeenth and eighteenth centuries various devices were proposed to sail the air ocean. Cyrano de Bergerac, a French writer of science fiction, imagined a square cabin with holes at top and bottom. He fitted a faceted crystal into the top hole to create a kind of vacuum within. Through the hole at the bottom air rushed in at furious speed to carry his space box aloft to the moon. Cyrano thought in modern terms, even though his theory was upside down. The crystal should have heated and expanded the air to send the capsule aloft by jet reaction.

A bishop in England played with the more modest idea that a flock of large geese could be harnessed to rise at the same instant. Twenty-five "goose power," it seemed to him, should be sufficient to carry aloft the weight of a man and his wicker carriage. Another bishop saw no reason why man could not practice flying with outstretched wings, as did the ostrich, with its leaps. In this way, he felt, longer and longer glides could be made. A blacksmith tried building a glider for him with two poles slung over his shoulders. Each pole-end had flapping rudders, which, by means of strings leading to ankles and wrists, opened and closed alternately, as the pilot "swam" through the air from a height.

So many wing-flapping tower-jumpers broke their bones that an Italian biologist, G. A. Borelli, was led to publish his researches into the flight of birds. He concluded that man, compared to birds, had such poor power-to-weight ratio in his chest muscles, it would always be impossible for him to fly by using his own strength.

Frustrated with their heavier-than-air devices, dreamers of flight turned to the possibilities presented by a lighter-than-air craft designed by an Italian Jesuit, Francisco de Lana, who went back to the idea of Bacon's copper globe. He conceived four such globes, twenty-five feet in diameter, and 1/225th of an inch thick, exhausted of air by means of a vacuum pump. He strung a boat under the globes and a sail between them, not realizing that such a sail would be useless. However, he did discern correctly the need for ballast to control ascent. To bring his boat down to earth again, he would uncock the globes, permitting air to enter them.

De Lana's machine might have been practical if it had been possible at that time to fabricate perfect copper globes that would not collapse from atmospheric pressure. But the father warned his readers not to build such an airship: "Where is the man who can fail to see that no city would be proof against surprise . . . iron weights could be hurled to wreck ships at sea, or they could be set on fire by fire balls and bombs; nor ships alone, but houses, fortresses and cities could be thus destroyed, with the certainty that the airship would come to no harm as the missiles could be hurled from a vast height."

The clergy of Portugal heeded this warning when a Brazilian friar, Bartolomao de Gusmao, presented a design for an airship to the King of Portugal in 1709. The design of his "Great Bird," as he called it, combined magic and science. What might be called scientific was the boatlike structure with rudders behind to steer it, with wings at the side to keep the ship upright, and with a parachute arrangement above to be floated by hot air. The magic consisted of magnets placed at aft and stern to pull up the body of the ship which was made of thin, iron plates. There was a net of wire, studded with amber beads, beneath the sails, to add "electric" attraction.

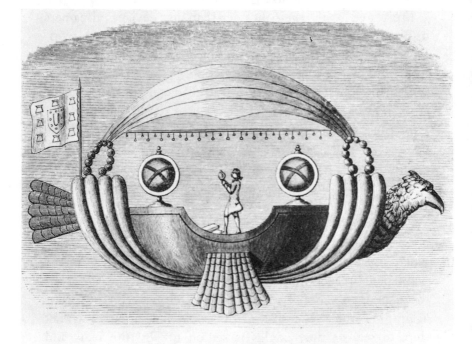

The proposed airship of Bartolomao de Gusmao.

In his enthusiasm Gusmao claimed that this airship could explore the earth and reach the North Pole in ten days. But the clergy accused him of having "devised a contrivance from which destruction and death would be hurled upon the cities of Christian men." Gusmao fled to Spain and was heard of no more.

Gusmao's unhappy experience persuaded the dreamers of science to write fantasies instead of creating new mechanical devices. Jonathan Swift made use of Gusmao's magnets and increased them to prodigious size to carry aloft a flying island, four-and-a-half miles in diameter and nine hundred feet thick.

A French writer, Joseph Galien of Avignon, imagined that his hero had found a way to rarify the air to the "ethereal" state that existed at the top of the atmosphere. He built a vast balloon of silk, ten times as large as Noah's Ark, enabling him to transport an army of ten thousand troops to Africa to conquer that continent.

The story was written in 1755. Eleven years later an English chemist succeeded in creating the extremely light gas which Roger Bacon had described as "liquid fire." The inventor was Henry Cavendish, an immensely wealthy recluse, already famous for having weighed the earth, analyzed the air, and revealed the composition of water.

He made a sensational report to the Royal Society of England. He had dropped chunks of iron into a dilute solution of sulphuric acid. The combination bubbled forth a gas, which Cavendish discovered was fourteen times lighter than air. However, it was so easily combustible, that he named it "inflammable air." Now we call it hydrogen. But when others tried to enclose the new gas, they found to their chagrin that the only container capable of holding it was a soap bubble.

It was a time of deep frustration among the scientists. They possessed the treasure of a gas lighter than air, only to find that it was too volatile and too dangerous. It diffused too rapidly through paper, linen or silk to be of use in aerial navigation. It would even combine with and chemically disintegrate the copper spheres of De Lana. When in contact with air, the smallest spark could set it burning.

Joseph (1740-1810) and Étienne (1745-1799) Montgolfier were sons of a paper manufacturer of Annonay, a town near Lyons, France. They read all the books of science related to air, such as Joseph Priestley's *Experiments and Observations of Different Kinds of Air* and the exciting reports on the combustible air of Henry Cavendish. They, too, tried to enclose hydrogen gas in various containers, but learned, as did others, that it seeped out too rapidly. However, they had developed the "prepared mind" so necessary to notice an unusual phenomenon and create an invention.

One day, Joseph threw a soiled paper bag into a fire. It swelled up with the thick smoke of the factory fire before the flames could reach it and floated up through the chimney. It struck Joseph that the fire must have contained a special gas that had the levitating property of hydrogen. Here was a mysterious gas that, unlike hydrogen, could be enclosed in a paper bag. At this time he might have remembered the words of Cyrano de Bergerac, "Since smoke by its nature ascends, I could have blown into an appropriate globe, a sufficient quantity to ascend with me."

With mounting excitement, Joseph and his brother Étienne experimented with all kinds of smoke and decided that the thick yellow smoke from burning wet straw and wool had the greatest upward tendency. They observed that the yellowish smoke was similar in appearance to clouds. They wondered if it might not be possible to enclose a small cloud in a bag large enough to contain it. They began enlarging the size of the bags and were delighted to find that the greater the volume, the more efficient the bags became, staying aloft

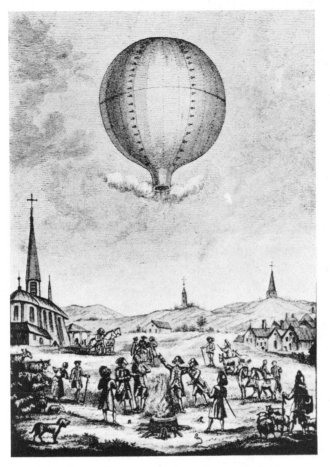

The first balloon ascent from Annonay, 1783.

longer and going higher.

The townspeople of Annonay watched with awe the aerostatic spheres floating over the rooftops. Every week the spheres grew bigger. The brothers finally decided to fabricate a globe big enough to enclose a cloud. Sensing that his sons had hit upon an important discovery, the father agreed to finance a public demonstration of a globe one hundred feet in circumference.

A great pit was dug in the public square, flanked by two high poles and scaffolding with ropes to hold down the inflated bag. On June 5, 1783, thousands of people from miles around assembled to watch the spectacle. They stared at the yellow sphere, its linen gores lined with paper, buttoned together, and with an open neck at the bottom which kept swallowing the smoke from the burning bonfire in the pit below. At last the tethered balloon began to tug at its ropes.

At a signal the ropes were cut and the balloon slowly, majestically began to ascend. The universal gasp of amazement was genuine. The huge sphere was being pulled up, it seemed, by an invisible string. At times, it seemed to be standing still. It ascended ever so gently a thousand feet, until it looked like a tiny gold coin against the silver masses of clouds. Ten minutes later, it descended with equal deliberation to the earth a mile and a half away. People exclaimed that nothing as miraculous had been seen since Creation.

The town council hurried away to send the astonishing report to the Academy of Science in Paris. The dreams of centuries had become a reality. A mantle of glory had descended on the little town of Annonay.

Golden Dawn

When the learned theoreticians of the Academy of Science read the report of the first balloon ascension, they felt both rapture and consternation. Never before had they read anything so sensational. But they found it incredible that the search of centuries had been fulfilled by mere outsiders, rank amateurs, with no status as scientists.

They immediately got in touch with Jacques A. C. Charles, professor of natural philosophy at the Sorbonne. Charles had good reason to feel dismay. He had just discovered a method, with the help of the Robert brothers, who were well-known instrument makers, to contain hydrogen within a silk bag by dipping the silk in a rubber varnish. At last, he could make use of the lightest of all gases to send aloft a balloon. That two unknown men from a little provincial town had beaten him to it, filled him with chagrin. Many a learned scientist was equally disconcerted.

When Charles read the report on the Montgolfier experiment more carefully, he discovered that the gas they had used had only half the lightness of air. It could not have been hydrogen, which weighed 5.3 pounds per 1000 cubic feet at sea level against the seventy-six pound weight of an equal volume of air—a one to fourteen ratio.

A friend of his, Professor Saint Fond, suggested that Charles should fabricate his hydrogen balloon immediately. There was such excitement about balloons, it would be easy to raise funds by public subscription. Lavoisier, another member of the Academy of Science, spoke up for the Montgolfier brothers. He felt that they should be invited to build a balloon in Paris. Enough money could be raised for both experiments. Besides, as a student of gases, Lavoisier was eager to discover the secret formula of the Montgolfier gas. Both suggestions were accepted, and the historic race between the Charles and the Montgolfier adherents began.

Charles decided to make a small model of a balloon, only thirteen feet in diameter. The gores of treated silk were quickly sewn together. An open neck permitted the escape of the gas as it expanded at higher altitudes. He filled a large barrel with water and iron filings in the courtyard of the Roberts' factory. By pouring in the "oil of vitriol" very carefully in small quantities, the "inflammable air" bubbled out little by little into the tube above the barrel that led through a hose into the neck of the *globe volant*. Charles handled it with the care that he would a dangerous explosive. After four days of this painstaking method, in constant fear of a sudden explosion, and always playing a hose on the surface of the bag to keep it cool and to prevent a too-rapid expansion of the gas, he at last saw the trial balloon swell up to its maximum.

Then he transferred the filled balloon by wagon in the dead of night to the Champs de Mars. Despite his secrecy many Parisians poured out of their homes to watch the weird procession. The balloon was launched the afternoon of August 27, 1783. Though there was a light drizzle, it shot up with great speed and disappeared in the distance, three thousand feet up. A gasp of amazement went through the throng.

One of the spectators was greatly disturbed. He was Étienne Montgolfier, who had just arrived in Paris at the invitation of the Academy of Science. He knew the bag was lifted by the most dangerous of gases, and he protested to the Academy that they had sponsored an experiment destined to bring fire and ruin to the countryside.

As a matter of fact, the hydrogen balloon did burst one hour later about twenty miles outside of Paris over the little village of Gonesse. When the peasants approached the mysterious object fallen from the skies, the ripped bag looked like the throat of a monster spewing its poisonous gas. It had the evil smell of sulphur that could only come from Hell. It bounced upon the ground as if it were alive. Two monks were hastily summoned. They made the sign of the Cross, pronounced the monster the handiwork of Satan, and bid it begone. The peasants attacked the stinking, bouncing

Drawing of peasants attacking the first hydrogen balloon, 1783.

dragon with pitchforks and flails, tied the lacerated monster to the tail of a horse, and dragged it triumphantly to the village square. Only then did the village priest find the notice attached to the bottom by Professor Charles, offering a reward for the return of the balloon to Paris. The balloon, after it was returned, was so damaged that Charles persuaded the King to issue an announcement informing the people not to be frightened of such objects.

Étienne Montgolfier had predicted the catastrophe, and he now went ahead to build his own balloon, which was in no danger of exploding. Charles explained that the Robert brothers had insisted on piping too much gas into the trial balloon against his own wishes. Then he made the bold claim that he would himself ascend when he completed his next balloon.

All of Paris had become air-minded with the ascension of the first Charles balloon. A few months later, when man himself decided to become airborne, the excitement became almost unbearable. This first conquest of the air took on the awe-inspiring dimensions of a momentous theatrical spectacle. Two different types of gases—smoke and hydrogen—clashed with each other for scientific and universal approval.

The hydrogen camp had suffered the first defeat when their balloon had burst. There was eager speculation about the Montgolfiers' secret formula. Their use of wet straw and wool to release a lifting gas brought a sense of the occult to their performance.

To dramatize the first ascension of the Montgolfier balloon in Paris, the brothers decided to make it an imposing mass seventy-four feet high. They went to lavish expense to decorate their aerostatic globe with all kinds of blue and gold symbols. The lemon-colored balloon dazzled the eyes of the spectators. The entire surface was decorated with fleur de lys at the top, eagles at the bottom, and in between the signs of the Zodiac, the initials of King Louis XVI, flaming suns, masks and garlands projected the brightly tinted gaiety of a Russian Easter egg.

The ascension was held at Versailles, with the King and court as spectators. At the last moment the Montgolfiers decided to add a basket carrying as the first passengers a truculent rooster, a frantic sheep and a puzzled duck.

The *Montgolfière* did not rise as high as the *Charlière*. It stayed aloft for only eight minutes. One of the ropes of the basket broke, and the balloon ignominiously landed on a treetop. The sheep, the duck and the cock in the basket, however, were found alive. The cock had an injured wing, but the Academy accepted the explanation that the sheep had stepped on it when the rope broke.

"What is the use of it all?" a friend asked the American ambassador to France, Benjamin Franklin, who sat in his carriage to watch the proceedings. Franklin replied, "Of what use is a baby?" On the whole, neither Charles nor the Montgolfiers could claim a victory. They made preparations for a more decisive second round. By this time the Montgolfiers realized that they had not discovered the kind of smoke which held clouds in suspension. The Academy explained that their bags rose because of the buoyancy of hot air. The second balloon of the Montgolfiers had a diameter of fifty-four feet and a capacity of 55,000 cubic feet. This time, they built a ring-shaped gallery with wicker rails at the bottom of the balloon, to carry the first human passengers. Below the gallery they suspended a wire cage in which a bonfire could be kept burning to keep up the buoyancy for a longer journey.

The King, disappointed by the first showing, doubted that human passengers would survive. The whole idea of air travel seemed risky. He suggested that there would be less risk of public anger if criminals under sentence of death were sent aloft.

A young nobleman, Pilatre de Rozier, did not agree, and

pleaded that he be allowed to go. Why should "two vile criminals have the first glory of rising in the sky?" His friend the Marquis d'Arlandes volunteered to accompany him. Preliminary tests were made with a tethered balloon. After rising with it to eighty-four feet, De Rozier felt it was important to enlarge the catwalk gallery from 210 to 330 feet— room enough for a larger bonfire. When completed, the balloon was seventy feet high and oval-shaped.

The Marquis d'Arlandes was a friend of the Duchesse de Polignac, a favorite of King Louis XVI. She persuaded the King to grant an interview to the Marquis, who pleaded eloquently for the King's permission for him to go up with De Rozier. "Would you deny the gentlemen of your kingdom," he asked, "the privilege of climbing nearer to God and thus showing to the world the glory of France!" The appeal was irresistible, and the King waved his permission: "Well, away to the heavens you go. May God go with you, and I give you my royal blessing. I wish I could escape from my temporal cares that easily."

This time, the great event was transferred to the Bois de Boulogne to accomodate the enormous crowd of spectators. The King, Marie Antoinette and the entire court assembled on that memorable day of November 21, 1783. The spectacle was made more dramatic with soldiers and cannons. The air was thick with the scent and the powder of courtiers' wigs. A cannon shot was the signal to release the ropes. The blue and gold manned balloon ascended between two flanking masts, rose to about 500 feet and floated over the rooftops.

The Marquis was so completely enchanted by the vision of Paris from above, that he was stupified with wonder. De Rozier woke him from his trance by shouting from the other end of the gallery to keep the grate fire burning. The sudden rapid descent of the balloon shocked the Marquis out of his spell. Frantically, they threw piles of straw and wool upon the fire and had it blazing. The Marquis heard a sound above

Artist's conception of Montgolfier and Charles balloons, 1783.

him. A rope had snapped. More horrifying, sparks from the flames had begun to eat black sparking holes in the linen-paper covering the balloon. They had prepared themselves with a bucket of water and sponges attached to long poles, and they succeeded in halting the danger in the nick of time. The blaze had lifted the balloon over Paris, across the Seine and over the open fields beyond the fortifications of the city.

They landed five miles from their starting point. The Marquis managed to jump out in time, but De Rozier was buried under the great mass of canvas that fell over him. When he emerged, he found himself surrounded by hysterical crowds, which had followed the twenty-minute journey all the way. The mob seized De Rozier's jacket, which he had removed because of the heat of the fire, and tore it into ribbons for souvenirs. The newspapers wrote of men traversing the world where only eagles flew. The press in every advanced country had difficulty in describing the aerial craft, calling it a *globe volant, aerostatique,* an aerostatic machine, a balloon and an aerostat.

The Montgolfiers were honored by the King in that day of glory. Pierre Montgolfier, the father, was given a patent of nobility with the Latin motto on his crest: "This is the way to the stars." His sons received a life pension of 600 livres, besides a grant of 40,000 livres for further experiments. That grant was to be used in the following year to build a *Montgolfière* of so great a dimension that seven men would be carried aloft over Lyons.

In the meantime Professor Charles had done a great deal of thinking about aerostatics. He had worked out mathematically just how much hydrogen might safely be funneled into the bag to permit expansion without bursting it. He added a gas escape valve on top, operated by a hanging rope, to make the balloon descend rapidly in an emergency. For ballast, he had the idea of taking up twenty-pound bags of sand. He decided to include a grapnel at the end of a rope for landing. He threw a net over the balloon that would hold up the gondola and distribute its weight evenly. He studied the barometer and figured a way to determine how high up he went. He tackled the problem of aerostatics from every possible angle, and with meticulous care he created the prototype of the free balloon as we know it today.

When Professor Charles announced that he and his friend Robert would rise with their second balloon on December 17, 1783, all of Paris declared a spontaneous holiday, closing all shops. For the first time, an entire population of a city, one half million people, crowded the great parade grounds of the Champs de Mars, and squeezing into every possible observation point, focused avid eyes on the red and white gores of the Charles balloon. Everyone asked the same question: Would it be able to rise without fire?

From early in the morning the great crowd watched the professor disposing wooden casks of diluted sulphuric acid around a large cistern. He had devised a more rapid method of conveying the gas into the balloon. Iron filings were dropped into the circle of casks. The resultant hydrogen gas bubbled out of the casks into the center cistern from where a long lead pipe led to the silk bag of the balloon. When the rubberized taffeta bag started to inflate, there was a murmur of apprehension. It all smacked of magic and medieval alchemy. The red stripes of the balloon looked sinister.

All was in readiness when a police officer struggled through the massed crowd to present Charles with a letter from the King forbidding the ascent. Montgolfier had convinced the King that the use of hydrogen was suicidal. The "inflammable air," once it burned, could not be doused with water, and it would burn down all of Paris.

This was an ascension for the people, who had supplied the funds for the spectacle, and they were not to be denied. As the news of the King's edict spread, the murmur grew into a menacing revolutionary growl. The professor gave his reply to the King: he would commit suicide then and there if permission for flight were not granted. The secret of the hydrogen balloon would be buried with him. There was a hush as the vast crowd waited for the reply from the King. A few minutes later a courtier rushed back with the King's blessing. There was a roar of acclamation.

The professor and his co-pilot, Robert, stepped onto the boat gondola which was attached to the rope netting belted around the middle of the balloon. The signal was given to fire the cannon. Soldiers presented arms, officers saluted. The ropes were released. Without fire or smoke, the balloon began to ascend swiftly. There was an entrancement of silence, and then spontaneous, multitudinous applause.

Charles was seen to throw out several handfuls of sand. Soon after, the balloon zoomed far above the launching site. Thousands of arms were raised in an ecstasy of happiness. Now, the red and white striped sphere seemed to be a messenger to infinity.

Later, Charles himself wrote that he had experienced an ecstasy like the vision of Heaven. He had imagined that he was living through a floating dream in which he stood still while the earth rapidly receded below him. "Nothing can approach the fascinating joy in my spirit as I felt that we were leaving the earth. It was not a simple pleasure. It was real joy. If only I had with me the last of our traducers, to say to him: 'See, incredulous man, how much is lost, if the progress of science is hindered.' "

"Oh, my dear friend," Charles exclaimed to his companion, "how happy we are! The sky belongs to us! What a breathtaking scene!" Then he first said the words that our astronauts were to say 180 years later: "I have never seen anything so beautiful before in my lifetime." And the half million spectators, identifying themselves with him, likewise felt for a few moments the sensation of divinity.

About two hours after his start, he pulled the rope which ran down through the inside of the balloon to the gondola. The valve on top was pulled open. The "inflammable air" was gradually released with a whistling noise into the atmosphere. The volume of the bag decreased and caused the balloon to descend. The weather was perfect, and he was able to alight gently in an open field near the little town of Nesle, twenty-five miles from Paris.

Still overcome by excitement, Charles asked his friend to make the report to the Academy in Paris. Even though the sun was beginning to set, Charles felt compelled to rise again in a first solo flight. The loss of his companion's weight caused the balloon to spring up with frightening swiftness. In twenty minutes he was out of sight of all terrestrial objects. There was much darkness below. Suddenly, he saw the sun again in full orb. He wrote: "At my setting out the sun was set on the valleys; he rose for me again . . . and I had the pleasure of seeing him set twice on the same day."

His barometer pointed to the astonishing height of 9,000 feet. He felt the stabbing pain of cold, but he continued his ascent to reach 10,500 feet. Then he experienced difficulty in breathing and a sudden intense agony of pain in his ears. He managed to pull the valve with his stiff frozen fingers.

When he finally landed, he was shaking with cold and felt ill. He knew now there was a barrier to the height a man in a balloon could go. It depressed him to think that there was a line beyond which man dared not trespass without the punishment of pain and possibly death.

The brave man never went up again. No one knows why. Perhaps he had experienced everything an aeronaut could experience. Perhaps he could see no further development for the balloon, for he had created a complete balloon which far surpassed the *Montgolfière*. Or, perhaps, Charles was the true scientist, one who sought always to cross new frontiers. He devoted his few remaining years to the mystery of the effect of light upon silver salts.

Balloonomania rose to a world-wide crescendo during the next three years. Benjamin Franklin pointed out the next step to be taken: ". . . Since man may be supported in the air, nothing is wanted but some slight handy instruments to steer and direct motion."

The Age of Innocence

THE AERIAL VOYAGE OF CHARLES MADE THE CIVILIZED WORLD
aware that an ocean of air 10,500 feet high had just been
opened for exploration. Monarchs demanded of their scientists
a demonstration of the "new science of aerostation," and the
next two years were to see as many as forty successful
ascents in the United States and Europe.

Man began to move through a third dimension. Toy balloons of rubberized silk and hydrogen floated away to the
music and dancing at garden parties. Apothecaries did a
rousing business selling packages of treated silk bags, an ounce
of oil of vitriol, and iron shavings. It became a popular sport
to pour the vitriol into water, add the shavings, and collect
the bubbles of hydrogen (known then as "combustible air")
into the receiving bag. Even the children of the poor busied
themselves with filling muslin bags with hot smoke to watch
the colored balloons float away.

The balloon shape dominated fashion and the decorative
arts. "Flying chariots" and "aerostatic globes" were stamped
on handkerchiefs, cards, dresses and chinaware. "You will
observe," Samuel Johnson wrote to a Mrs. Thrale, "that the

balloon engages all mankind." It was a joyous period. Launched only in perfect weather, the aerial spheres rose as softly and effortlessly as soap bubbles. To onlookers it seemed that sky currents higher up were as constant as rivers.

Because the balloon moved at the same speed as the air current in which it was suspended, the pilot felt no sensation of wind. It was a strange experience to fly with the wind and yet feel no wind. Nor was there any awareness of movement, even in a sixty mile an hour gale. From high up the earth had the restful shape of a saucer. Air transport was certainly the easiest and most comfortable way to go from one place to another. The rapture of moving on this frail aerial bark was such that "the soul might almost fancy it had passed the confines of the grave."

There was every reason to believe that the balloon would soon become a universal conveyance. Hope was everywhere that the rivers in the sky would be able to waft passengers across oceans and continents. George Washington wrote with awe, "Our friends in Paris, in a little time, will come flying thro' the air instead of ploughing the ocean to get to America." Benjamin Franklin imagined a horse, slung under a small globe, being able to make wondrous leaps across the countryside, jumping easily over hedges and ditches.

Jefferson predicted that man would soon be able to travel as fast as the wind across the face of the earth—traversing deserts, conveying intelligence into besieged places and transporting all kinds of commodities. The North Pole, itself, would be only a day's journey away.

According to Franklin the "light, handy instruments" to make such locomotion possible need only be similar to the sails and rudders of ships. The Academy of Lyons organized a prize competition for the steering of a balloon. Ninety-six "solutions" were entered, among them a method of steering by hitching silk cords to eagles.

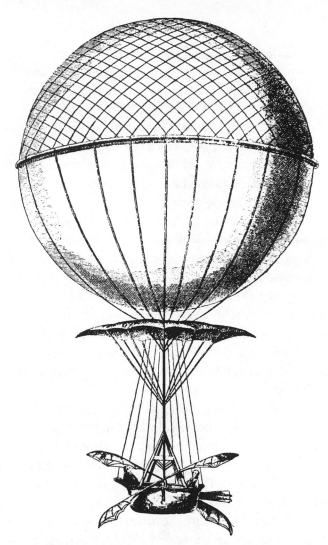

Drawing of Blanchard's *vaisseau volant*.

The problem challenged the imagination of a Frenchman, François Blanchard, who built a *vaisseau volant*. He placed a lightweight car, a sort of tented houseboat, with four great oval flappers and huge rudders under a balloon. As a safety feature, he added an open parachute between gondola and bag. He worked the flappers in vain. They had no influence on the movement of the balloon. Chagrined, he cut the bag, determined to test his parachute. It checked his speed as it plunged downward, and Blanchard suffered only a broken leg.

Blanchard worked heroically all through 1784, trying out all kinds of manual devices. His was the world's first attempt to propel an aircraft by whirling a fan. It seemed incredible to him that such a nothingness as air offered so much resistance to his "light, handy instruments." He was so determined to conquer the wind that he became the most persistent rower, flapper and paddler of his time.

Inventors worked feverishly with all sorts of new devices. Every possible category of mechanical motion was tried out: screw propellers, spirals, sails, countersails, and even a paddle wheel contraption whose blades revolved halfway around and halfway backward. Registering nothing but failure, the experimenters became more desperate. They tried out explosions of gunpowder to achieve recoil force, jets of compressed air, jets of steam.

It became despairingly clear: there was no way to get a balloon to move against the wind. The slightest current of air exercised too easy an influence on the enormous mass of the sphere. The shape of the balloon made no difference: round, conical, cylindrical and conjoined shapes were equally without effect. Some winds were perverse enough to rotate the bag playfully and oscillate the car. The wind, so seemingly gentle and friendly in perfect weather, soon revealed itself as a great antagonist. Blanchard decided finally that he would master Nature by submitting to it. He would make use of the force of the wind to attempt a spectacular long-distance journey: the crossing of the English Channel.

Jeffries, an American physician who had exiled himself because he was an ardent Royalist, offered the financial backing to Blanchard. Exhaustive preparations were made for the great expedition across the thirty miles of water. The cargo included barometer, compass, anchor, flags, cork jackets, brandy, biscuits, apples, pamphlets and thirty pounds of ballast. Blanchard could not resist making one last attempt to master the wind. He added large silk-covered oars and a hand-operated revolving fan, called a *moulinet*. This added weight overloaded the balloon. Nevertheless, Dr. Jeffries insisted upon accompanying Blanchard. Since the doctor had paid one hundred guineas to be the first passenger on a Channel crossing, Blanchard was legally obliged to take him along.

That first aerial journey across the Channel was launched from the Dover cliffs. The sky was full of cumulus clouds, which to an experienced balloonist today means strong down-drafts alternating with strong updrafts. To correct the down-run, Blanchard threw out his sand. The effect a few minutes later was a sudden swift upward movement. To escape the dangerous updraft, he valved too much hydrogen and the bag moved down precipitously. To escape hitting the water, they threw everything overboard—*moulinet*, oars, instru-ments, rope, anchor, the lining of the basket and most of their clothes—which shot the balloon up again. They were riding a balky, bouncing, bumptious Pegasus. Within sight of the French coast, they clung to the ropes and were prepared to cut off their basket when a sudden updraft took them over the cliffs and beyond. Brushing against the tops of trees, they were able finally to snatch at branches to halt their flight.

Even at best a balloon landing is a controlled accident. It had been a rough-and-tumble two-hour voyage and it ended ignominiously. Blanchard and Jeffries borrowed clothes from peasants and rode a bumping wagon to Calais, much dis-heartened. The welcome they received there, the acclaim and rapture of the multitude, astounded them. In Paris King Louis XVI awarded Blanchard a purse of twelve thousand francs, and a pension of twelve hundred francs.

The success of the English Channel crossing in 1785 inspired Pilatre de Rozier to attempt a longer journey, this time from France to England. The man who had been the first to fly created a new kind of balloon for his next historic voyage. He knew that rubberized fabric leaked too much gas and would not suffice for a long journey. Why not combine a hydrogen balloon with a hot-air *Montgolfière*, which could carry a fire and be stoked continuously in mid-air, prolonging the journey? It seemed to be a sensible procedure to have two balloons sustain the basket.

The *Rozière*, as he named it, had a spherical hydrogen-filled bag above a vertical cylinder. The air in the cylinder could be kept warm by feeding a fire in the brazier beneath it. Since he expected to ascend very high, it was logical to put a woodburning stove in the basket as a protection against the icy cold of the atmosphere.

Full of hope, De Rozier and his companion, P. A. de Romans, launched from Boulogne for England in a brisk wind that was moving in the right direction. Soon afterwards they met with an unforseen difficulty. The wind shifted, tossed them about in turbulent air currents, and kept them circling above their starting point. The sphere-above-cylinder shape of the *Rozière* caused the basket to oscillate like a pendulum, overturning the wood-burning stove.

The wicker basket caught fire. They stamped out the flames, and tried to throw the stove over the edge of the basket. They were unaware that the sparks had reached the escaping hydrogen and that a blue-violet tongue of flame had begun licking the hydrogen bag. The *Rozière* burst into flames. Like Icarus, De Rozier plunged down to the surf below, landing only three feet from the beach of Boulogne.

The appalling tragedy put an end to the first fine rapture of that aerial age of innocence. The enthusiastic hope of Benjamin Franklin for world-wide aerial transportation gave way to the blunt realism of Samuel Johnson. He predicted that ballooning would never prove to be more than a mere pastime, since nobody could ever invent a balloon that would rise higher than a mountain, or that could be steered in any desired direction. This mood of baffled hopelessness and cruel disappointment lasted for decades.

Then a brilliant military engineer Jean Baptiste Meusnier read a paper before the French Academy of Science, *Equilibrium of Air Machines*, which suggested a way out of the dilemma. He pointed out the need for a suitable power engine that could whirl propellers with more force than was possible by the use of muscles or clockwork mechanisms. He revealed that steering might be made possible with a larger tail rudder, and that little ballonets of hydrogen could be encompassed in a larger envelope filled with air to preserve its shape. Meusnier persuaded the Robert brothers to build such an elongated dirigible, but the weight of the enclosed air cancelled its buoyancy.

Meusnier's report was buried by the coming of the French Revolutionary Wars, and he, who was then a general, was killed in the Battle of Mayence in 1793. Even in the midst of all these early frustrations the balloon played a useful part in the wars. The French army had organized a balloon corps against the invading Austrian army. The tethered balloon, the *Entreprenant*, was able to point out the movement of enemy troops and locate the artillery. It helped make possible the French victory in the Battle of Fleurus.

Napoleon kept two balloon companies in training. A new method of passing steam over hot iron as a swifter way of obtaining hydrogen made it possible to inflate balloons quickly over a battlefield. Just before the Battle of Waterloo, Napoleon had assembled all the materials necessary to build a fleet of balloons. It was destroyed by the enemy before it could be used. If Napoleon had been able to use his balloons in this battle, he might have been forewarned of Blucher's advance and taken quicker countermeasures. For the lack of a balloon an empire was lost.

Balloon in use in the Battle of Fleurus, 1794.

Flying Man

SPECULATION DESERVES A PLACE IN ANY HISTORY OF TECH-
nology. Without dreams there is no vision. A popular fantasy
of the seventeenth century, Campenella's *City of the Sun*,
mentioned that the happy dweller of that Utopia traveled in
wagons fitted with sails that were borne along by the wind.
This image was destined to have a surprising historical development. It inspired a wealthy Dutch mathematician, Simon
Stevenius, to build a wind-driven wagon. A strong wind raced
it over the flat, hard sands of Holland's shore at the unheard
of speed of twenty-two miles an hour.

The sailing wagon stirred the enthusiasm of the first secretary of the Royal Society of England, John Wilkins. He noted
the phenomenal speed in his *Mathematical Magic*, a popular
book of 1648. A host of readers read his comments that
Stevenius should have done something more imaginative with
the sails of his wagon. If he had built them like a windmill's
arms and placed one windmill of sails horizontally above and
another vertically behind the wagon, the wind would have
sent it soaring as an aerial carriage.

As if to prove that no good idea is ever really lost, a French

33

mathematician twenty years later, actually designed such a flying machine. A. J. P. Paucton claimed that his aerial carriage needed no wind; that it could be rowed aloft by muscle power. The design inspired François Blanchard to build an air vehicle that could be made to soar by muscular power. He placed a large rudder behind his enclosed vessel for steering. Projecting from the vessel were four flappers; above the vessel huge wings for balancing. He operated the surfaces with levers and foot pedals. He explained that he failed to get it off the ground only because he could not move the flappers fast enough. Swiftness of movement, he claimed, was the key to flight. The idea was finally taken up by the Academy of Science, when Coulombier, a mathematician, concluded 12,000 square feet of surface, flapping at a speed of three feet a second, would be needed to raise a flying vessel.

The controversy stirred Restif de la Bretonne, the most prolific writer of his time, to dash off a story about a flying man in 1781. Victorin, the hero of the story, was a penniless young man of noble sentiments, a rebel against the arrogance and vanity of the aristocrats. He was in love with Christine, inaccessible to him because of her wealthy parents. She was pure in heart and loved him in turn, but only a miracle could bring heiress and peasant together in marriage.

Victorin accomplished the miracle by inventing a flying suit. The original illustration of this flying suit suggests the military rocket belt with its twin jet hydrogen peroxide pro-

Victorin in his flying suit.

pulsion system mounted on the back of a fibreglass corset being designed today for soldiers.

This superman of 1781 acted with the boldness of today's comic strip hero. While Christine and her parents were on the way to church, he swooped down like the roc of the Arabian Nights and snatched away his beloved. To everyone's amazement, he flew off with her to an aerial nest he had created for her atop a mountain. This theme of love and freedom and winging through the air was irresistible and helped stir an entire generation to become air-minded. A year after the book was published, half of Paris saw a man soaring in a balloon.

The following year, a flying toy invented by Launoy and Bienvenue, became the rage. The toy had feathers stuck in corks at both ends of a stick that was set in a bow: By looping a string around the stick, children could wind the stick and the bow in opposite directions, until the bow became taut enough to be released. The stick unwound rapidly, whirling the feathers that lifted the flying machine straight up in the air.

This mechanical marvel was considered important enough to be demonstrated before the French Academy of Science. Why could it not be made life-size to lift a man? Thus, one year after the invention of the balloon, rivalry sprang up between lighter and heavier-than-air flight that was to stir the world for the next 150 years. It started a young man of genius, George Cayley of England, to wonder if the laws of mechanics might not bring to reality the dreams and speculations of flight.

The flying toy of Launoy and Bienvenu.

Just as Leonardo Da Vinci's aeronautic notes, hidden for centuries, were not translated and published until 1893, George Cayley's scientific papers on heavier-than-air flight written in 1809 were not fully understood until our own day. Historians now recognize that the story of aviation must give more space than has before been allocated to the man who laid the foundations of aerodynamics (the science which deals with the forces acting on bodies in motion through the air) for airplane flight. A vast gulf separates Cayley's glider of 1808 from the tower-jumpers who wafted on home-made wings through the centuries only to break their bones. It is the gulf that separates speculation from scientific analysis.

Unlike Victorin, George Cayley had the advantages of wealth and a mother who was an artist with a wide-ranging intellect and non-conforming views. She chose brilliant tutors for her son. During his college years he had distinguished scientists giving him lessons in experimental science. Cayley, who had spent more time in a watchmaker's shop during his youth than in his school, was able to pursue his passion for invention with a thorough knowledge of navigation, mathematics, mechanics and physics.

He improved the efficiency of the Launoy helicopter toy by doubling the number of feathers. His tutor, seeing the toy, brought to his notice the words of Roger Bacon (1214-1292), "to make engines for flying, a man [must sit] . . . in the midst thereof . . . turning an instrument, which moves artificial wings made to beat the air much after the fashion of a bird's flight." The words started him thinking of making the helicopter toy life-size, capable of lifting a man. Might it not be possible to use the laws of mechanics to make a reality of Bretonne's flying man, just as others had used the laws of mechanics to improve the velocity of windmill sails?

As part of his education, Cayley had been given a thorough understanding of the instruments devised by engineers to measure wind pressures. He had studied the swinging arm, invented by Benjamin Robins (1707-1751), to test the speed of projectiles fired out of a gun. The same whirling arm had been used by R. L. Edgeworth (1744-1817) to determine the force of the wind against sheets of tin. It was Edgeworth who found that tilting the sheets gave them greater velocity, and led to the reshaping of the flat windmill sails.

John Smeaton (1724-1792) used the whirling arm to study the direct resistance of air on cloth surfaces. He discovered that curved surfaces gave more lift to sails than straight ones, and thus further improved the windmills of England. Cayley knew of all of this, and of other similar experiments, and with this learning he had acquired a devotion to the precise language of mathematics instead of vague speculative explanations. He was trained in direct observation, controlled experiments, the logic of mathematics. He knew he was not yet ready to enlarge his toy into a man-carrying vehicle.

Garnerin's 1797 leap in a parachute from a balloon 2,000 feet above Paris enraptured the twenty-four-year-old Cayley. It was the first successful leap from such a height in history. In that romantic era, the parachutist was transformed by the populace into Victorin flinging himself from a mountain top. There was one disturbing note, however. Garnerin's basket was attached by cords to a huge umbrella-shaped parachute that swung it back and forth like a pendulum, causing the daring hero to suffer airsickness. It was the kind of mechanical problem that delighted Cayley.

The parachute of Garnerin.

Cayley concluded that Garnerin had used the worst possible form for his parachute invention. The pressure of the air trying to force its way out of the umbrella enclosure kept it tipping and swinging. He figured the pressure of air would have been smoother if the umbrella shape had been inverted, with the apex at the bottom instead of at the top.

Nature had dictated this v-shape in birds' wings. Cayley's sharp eyes had noted that slight v-shape angle in sycamore seeds where the two wings met each other. They never lost their horizontal stability as they spun downward, sometimes for a distance of sixty yards, even on a calm day. Why could not a parachute be made with the same dihedral v-shaped angle?

It was a leap of the imagination to transform the passive parachute into a giant sycamore seed, or, for that matter, into a huge skimming bird. But Cayley was too knowledgeable a student of mechanics to construct what he called a "governable parachute" by guess. He understood that he would have to determine mathematically the precise forces involved.

His imagination jumped from this to an experiment never before attempted: a study of the pressures on birds' wings and kites. In this way, he might solve the problem of steering an aerial craft. A heavier-than-air device, a "governable parachute," would be more adaptable for steering than a gas bag.

It was a dizzying vision. A flying surface, like the flying carpet of the Arabian Nights, could be made into a vehicle that could be steered through the air. Just as Galileo laid the theoretical foundations of force and motion, Cayley would be the first to clarify the fundamentals of heavier-than-air flight. Sensing the scientific importance of his revelation, he decided to keep a notebook, the first page of which read, "You, to whom it may concern, when I am gone, may find the seeds of thoughts in these scrawls." Cayley had the feeling, rightfully, that his notebook would make history.

First Airplane in History

IN THE FIRST FLUSH OF HIS INSPIRATION, CAYLEY MADE A tentative test on how to control a surface that was moving through the air. He had been a passionate kite flyer as a child, and now he began his experiments with kites. He attached a kite surface to a pole and flung it like a javelin down the gently sloping hills of Brompton Hall, his estate. It nose dived far too quickly.

Remembering that the swinging arm experiments had revealed that a tilted surface moved at a greater velocity than a flat surface with the same applied force, Cayley tilted his kite with a small supporting stick over the central pole. Instead of a kite's tail, he placed a smaller kite on the rear of the supporting pole for longitudinal stability. Then, he positioned a vertical surface over the rear kite at a fixed angle to serve as a steering rudder as was done with ships.

He flung his contraption over the crest of the hill and saw it fly a surprising distance in the direction given it by the angle of the rudder. It encouraged him to work on refinements. He learned to attach a tail piece to a universal joint so that its surfaces could be more readily adjusted at different angles. He was now able to bend the horizontal surface in the rear downward to prevent his craft from pitching down too soon.

He made larger constructions with greater wing areas, using a tow rope to launch them in the air. He hung various weights on the center of a supporting pole to see how much weight the wing surface would carry. He found that a 54 square foot area would carry 125 pounds without breaking the fragile wing of bamboo canes and linen. He became aware that the cloth wing billowed in flight, proving, as had one of the swinging arm experiments, that a camber (a curved surface) accelerated the lifting capacity and the velocity. As he achieved greater and greater distances of flight, he knew he was moving in the direction of complete control.

How much wing area would it take to support a man of 150 pounds? According to Smeaton's swinging arm experiment, a square foot of surface of a windmill sail riding the wind was able to support a pound of weight. Cayley calculated that 500 square feet of cloth surface with its bamboo poles would weigh no more than fifty pounds. He found that this weight, proportionally, was three times lighter than the weight of the wings of a goose. Thus 500 square feet of surface should be able to carry the 300 pounds that would comprise the weight of a pilot, of the glider, and of the flappers and other devices needed to swing them up and down.

He had reached the point where he could conceive of a pilot in a car pushing a lever back and forth to transmit energy to flapping wings beneath the main wings. He could make real what Bretonne could only imagine with a flying man and what Blanchard was unable to do with his flying vessel. In one burst of feverish activity he had conceived the essentials of an airplane with flapping wings.

His imagination and his technical knowledge had created the air craft of the future. To make sure that posterity would never lose this astonishing vision, he searched for something more durable than his notes on paper. He decided instead to etch a design on a silver disc. Like the stone tablets of the ten commandments, it would reveal the aerodynamic laws that could bring to man a new destiny—the conquest of the skies with a heavier-than-air machine.

On one side, he engraved an arrow touching an inclined line that supported a balanced triangle. The hieroglyphic could be interpreted by later generations with mathematical knowledge. They would understand that a force can make a surface (the inclined line) support a given weight (the triangle) by the application of power (the arrow) to the resistance of air. Future scientists would read in these geometric lines the revelation that a system of lift was distinct and separate from other forces.

To make his meaning clearer, he etched on the other side of the disc, what he conceived to be the configuration of a future air machine. He gave the main wing a camber. Below it, he outlined a sheltered boat embracing the figure of a pilot. The tail piece, comprising horizontal and vertical surfaces, was attached to the supporting pole by means of a universal joint that could be made to turn in any direction to balance and steer the machine in the air. As a final touch, he introduced a method of flapping by muscular exertion. The pilot holds a lever in the right hand. Turned back and forth it could waft flappers dimly outlined at his left, in an up and down motion.

This etching presented the outline of an airplane that still holds true in form. Engraved on silver in 1799, it is today enshrined in the Science Museum of London.

There was still much work to be done before theory could become a practical air machine. But Cayley had too little time to spare for experimenting. His father had died, and he had the responsibility of managing the farmlands of a great Yorkshire estate. He had married the daughter of his first private tutor; there were children and family obligations. The man of affairs was in conflict with his creative, speculative mind.

Like Leonardo Da Vinci before him, all kinds of mechanical dreams and enterprises vied for his attention. During his life of eighty-four years he agitated against slavery, proposed political reforms, served in Parliament, originated new methods to drain flooded lands, created an artificial hand for the maimed, and developed new railway equipment, lifeboats and caterpillar tractors. While working on his glider, he invented and patented streamlined gun shells for the defense of his country against the threatened invasion of Napoleon.

A second sensational parachute jump of Garnerin in 1802 over London from a balloon height of 8,000 feet communicated a new excitement to Cayley. The wild, whirling words of Garnerin, describing the sensations of floating through the air, inspired Cayley to continue his aeronautic research.

He began by building a whirling arm. It was supported on a tripod. The central pole of the arm was turned with wires connected to a pulley and a crank. The turning crank rotated the five-foot whirling arm on top at high speeds. The top lever-arm had a balanced weight at one end and a bird's wing, or cloth surface, on the other end. Rotation of the arm permitted a circular flight for anything put on the wheel of about 600 feet.

His first experiments confirmed Smeaton's previous calculation of a pound of lift for every square foot of surface. But Cayley began to observe new phenomena. If the speed were doubled, the amount of lift available increased fourfold. Tilting the surface at a six-degree angle doubled the lifting capacity even with the same applied force. Thus it was confirmed that the force of lift was something distinct and separate from the resistance of air to a flying object.

Just how did the force of lift work? He divined that the swift flow of air over the surface and behind the wing created a kind of vacuum, permitting the normal pressure below to lift up the surface. It was this force of lift that kept a gliding bird skimming without the need of flapping its wings constantly. It was the same force that pushed the kite up into the sky. Most important of all, it encouraged the idea that comparatively slight power would be required to sweep a mechanical flying object through the air. A lightweight engine, with a small amount of horsepower, could accomplish the miracle of flight.

He calculated that the lightest practical steam engine available then would weigh 163 pounds, too heavy for his purpose. He needed a source of energy that had "the power of a horse and the weight less than that of a man."

He saw clearly that the engine was the stumbling block to aeronautical navigation. From then on he spent more time trying to perfect a new engine than he did on the problems of aerodynamics. In fact, he inspired almost every great engineer in England to attempt the light and powerful engine that would take the place of steam. But since no such engine seemed forthcoming for all his efforts, for his further air experiments Cayley had to depend on the muscular power of a pilot.

He had observed that birds bent the ends of their feathers downwards, but never backwards. A device to operate flapping wings by pushing a lever back and forth was easier to construct than a device to operate propellers, as had been done for balloons. Cayley felt that the first whirling propeller, the *moulinet* of Blanchard, had proven too weak to be useful. For Cayley, flapping wings seemed to be more practical.

But even the flapping device proved to be difficult. It had to move more rapidly, as Blanchard had pointed out, than the thirty-five-mile velocity of a glider sweeping downhill. Anything less would just increase the resistance of the body through the air. To improve the rapidity of the up and down motion, he gave each of his two flappers an alternate motion; as one moved up, the other pushed down.

To save weight became a vital necessity. He discovered that the spindle shape of a bird's body gave it only half the air resistance of a sphere. Such a spindle shape offered least resistance to the flow of air. Cayley was the first to grasp the importance of streamlining.

Then, again, his experiments on the swinging arm revealed to him that the center of pressure on the wing moved as the wing moved. A six-degree camber permitted less of this shifting movement than did deeper curves. He calculated just how far ahead the center of gravity must be to the center of pressures to keep the surface stable through the air. To check all of this he built gliders. By 1804 he had a model glider that could be automatically steered across a valley. He wrote:

"It was beautiful to see this noble white bird sail majestically from the top of a hill to any given point of the plain below it, with perfect steadiness and surface, according to the set of the rudder, merely by its own weight, descending in an angle of about eight degrees with the horizon."

The success of his model glider stirred Cayley into a state of feverish anticipation. His next step was to build a glider big enough to support a man. New problems loomed up. He had to find a way to attain flying speed without the use of a tow rope. So large a glider could not be towed through the air as the small ones were. He conceived of an under-carriage of three wheels. Since the wooden spokes of wheels were too heavy, he substituted for them tight cords, creating the forerunner of the bicycle wheel. He solved the problem of the take-off run with an open center section in his glider. Using his wheeled under-carriage, a pilot could run forward within the vehicle and give it a flying start just under the crest of the hill.

When the new glider was built, a mechanic ran forward in it at full speed. Taking advantage of a gentle breeze, he was lifted up so strongly, he was scarcely able to touch the ground. When a boy ran with the glider, he found himself lifted for several yards. Now it needed only flappers to make it a flying machine. Cayley had concluded that he could duplicate the movements of a bird's wings by giving his flappers a waft of four feet a second. The pilot would push and pull the lever at a speed of 42.5 feet a second. Since the glider would be flying on its own at thirty-five feet a second, the extra speed of the flappers could be added to the propelling and lifting force.

When Cayley tested his new mechanism by sitting in it and rowing the levers, he found that the flappers lifted his own weight and that of the glider a few inches off the ground. He was convinced now that a strong pilot would have the two horsepower necessary to propel the winged machine for several minutes. In his notebook he wrote these words of triumph: "There is no doubt of the thing being accomplished."

What followed is shrouded in mystery. In his notes, Cayley mentions only that his glider was destroyed accidentally. He quoted Plautus, the ancient Roman, "flying without feathers is not easy."

In 1808 Cayley was thirty-five years of age. With the momentum and success in aeronautics he had already attained, it is inconceivable that he would have dropped his project so abruptly except for very grave reasons. Had he not written, "success can be hoped for only after repeated blunders?" Was his glider destroyed by another? Did he intend to fly himself and thus create an emotional storm in his home? Did he neglect his estate to a point of financial difficulty? Did his failure to create a suitable engine doom the enterprise for him? No one knows. We only know that for the next four decades he interested himself only in dirigibles.

Cayley never intended to publish his findings until he could demonstrate a manned flight before the world. A sensational item in 1809 suddenly changed his mind. A clockmaker of Vienna, J. Degen, demonstrated a flying machine consisting of two umbrella-shaped wings that folded up and extended. By beating the wings rapidly, "the flying man of Vienna" was reported to have risen fifty-four feet. There was tremendous press excitement. The dream of Bretonne had become real at last.

Inexcusably, the report failed to mention that Degen's apparatus was slung beneath a small balloon, and that the balloon was tethered to a rope to prevent it from flying away. He had only to waft the wings down to push the machine up. The balloon accounted for ninety pounds of lift of the one hundred and ninety pounds needed to lift him into the air. Cayley, however, became convinced that another had succeeded and had snatched from him the crown of victory. He hastened to write an account of his own experiments to let the world know of his priority in the matter.

Degen's apparatus as Cayley saw it, without the balloon.

His classic paper, "On Aerial Navigation," was published in three issues of *Nicholson's Journal* of 1809-1810. His articles were a masterful survey of the mathematical relationships and theoretical insights required to make a surface support a given weight when power was applied to overcome the resistance of air. The scientific principles were spelled out, even though a light enough engine to supply the necessary power to fly distances did not exist. It is an astonishing record, spun out of his mind through ten years of labor, at the very beginning of the conquest of the air.

The magazine articles did not generate the mass excitement that Cayley had hoped for. The mathematical reasoning was far above the head of the average reader. The great contemporary engineers praised him for his important insights but did not encourage him to follow through. No one even suggested the usefulness of gliding as a prelude to powered airplane flight. Later that year, a journalist, Thomas Walker, wrote a popularization entitled *A Treatise Upon the Art of Flying by Mechanical Means*. No credit was given to Cayley when the book became a best seller in 1810. A flying machine had the romantic interest of a fantasy. It was something fascinating to read about, but no one expected that it might have any future. Decades of silence settled over the idea of heavier-than-air flight.

The Steerable Balloon

THE CROWDS COULD BE EXCITED ONLY BY BALLOONS. SAMUEL Johnson had said of balloons, "In amusement, mere amusement, I am afraid it must end, for I do not find that its course can be directed so that it shall serve any useful purpose in communication." When Blanchard failed to steer a balloon, a gas bag became a gaudy bubble in the hands of exhibition makers. But the nineteenth century loved them.

After Blanchard's death, his widow supported herself by going up in balloons at fairs to the accompaniment of a dazzling display of fireworks.

One fatal day, a rocket misfired and hit the hydrogen bag. The bottom of the bag caught fire. The top fabric of the bag had remained intact, embraced as it was by the net, and it thus served as a parachute to check the swiftness of descent. The brave woman in her basket gaily waved her flags, and it seemed to the spectators that she had added a new attraction to her performance as she descended over the rooftops of Paris. The basket swung against a roof, turned over and tumbled Madame Blanchard to the pavement two stories below. Her back was broken, and she died on the way to the hospital.

She had not died in vain. Aeronauts marvelled at the slowness of her descent after the fire had made a parachute out of the balloon. Garnerin's descent under a parachute and the slow descent of a balloon in flames brought a new hope that falls from great heights need not be fatal.

An American, John Wise, tested this possibility by cutting his gas bag at a great height. The gas emptied and the bag floated up to the top of the net to form a kind of parachute. Wise was able to float down gently. Growing bolder, he rose three miles up in the air and fired a gun into his bag. The explosion emptied the bag of all its gas. The fabric remained, still embraced by the net, again acting as a parachute. The daredevil felt the wind on his face and he knew he was going straight down at too rapid a pace. A few feet from the ground, he managed to jump to safety.

He demonstrated this performance several times, convincing the press of the world that ballooning had become a safe and jolly hobby. It led Wise in 1839 to invent another safety device—the rip panel. One hard pull from a rip cord removed a specially glued covering in the top section of the balloon. It opened up a big enough hole for all the hydrogen to escape rapidly, making it possible for the bag to collapse suddenly about twenty-five feet above the ground for a quick landing. It proved to be an effective safety precaution against the dragging, bouncing danger of a strong ground wind.

Thus, two generations after Charles' historic flight, aeronauts had made some small conquests in the newly found highway of air, and had lost much of the fear that had kept Charles from ever wanting to fly again. Cayley, himself, began in 1816 to think about balloons, because it seemed even to him that balloon navigation would be an accomplished fact before a practical airplane could be developed. His experiments in aerodynamics had proved to him that a globe was not the best shape to overcome air resistance. Like a ship, a steerable balloon should have a "cod's head and a mackerel tail."

A cylinder shape, he concluded, offered only one third the resistance to air that a sphere did. But to streamline a balloon into a cylindrical shape offered difficulties. The internal pressure of expanding hydrogen would tend to blow up a cylinder into a globe again. So Cayley began a long series of experiments to determine how to keep the shape of an elongated balloon. He began with the idea of enclosing a balloon of hydrogen within a larger elongated balloon filled with air, which would hold its shape. Later he recommended thin, metallic sheets or internal bracing. Out of his studies of pressures and flowing air, he realized that the larger the gas container, the higher its efficiency in lift. The payload gets better as the airship gets bigger. He was certain that the giant dirigible would become the first practical air transport in the future.

He finally went on to design the prototype of what was to become the Zeppelin of the twentieth century. He reasoned that if a dirigible could be made gigantic enough, it could support a heavy steam engine and a structure of internal cross bracings to keep its shape. The giant bag could be subdivided into ballonets, so that the failure of one need not doom the entire airship. His design was of an airship four hundred and thirty-two feet in length holding five million cubic feet of gas. This required twelve thousand square yards of fabric and a 100 horsepower steam engine. A large enough rudder turned by a boom on either side would steer the ship. A movable weight slung along the bottom was intended to regulate the up and down movement. So large a ship would have a payload of 34 tons, making possible the transport of 50 men at 15 miles per hour for 720 miles in 24 hours.

The building of such a ship could be financed only by a national subscription, and Cayley sought three different times to organize a national aeronautic society and failed. However, his letters to the press on this subject did have an influence on Mary Shelley, who was already famous for her sensational book *Frankenstein.* Her new novel, *The Last Man,* became the best seller of the 1820's. The story was laid in the future of 2092 A.D., when a universal plague had left the world desolate of humanity. Verney, the sole survivor, searches the world for other survivors in a steerable passenger dirigible traveling from city to city.

The dream of a steerable balloon also fired the enthusiasm of young Charles Green. He yearned to become an aeronaut, but the expense of hydrogen seemed to make this impossible. Then the idea occurred to him that cheap coal gas, beginning to be used for lighting cities, might serve as a substitute. Green filled a tiny bag with this new gas and discovered it had half the lightness of air, sufficient to float a balloon.

Soon after launching himself upon a career that was eventually to set a record of 500 ascensions, he made another brilliant discovery. He came across a pamphlet, written in 1794 by a Mr. Deverell, that spelled out a new way of controlling the height of a balloon. An aeronaut could take a reel of weighted rope with him and unwind it as he mounted. By using this device, Green could eliminate the need for frequent valving of gas to keep the balloon from going too high. With the help of a winch, he could pull a heavy rope and its weight at the end up or down to keep his balloon at the level he desired. Certain of saving his gas, he was in a position to attempt a long distance voyage. He found in Monck Mason a financial backer.

Green fabricated his red and yellow silk balloon so carefully that it remained in service for more than forty years. Besides Monck Mason, Robert Holland, a member of Parliament, joined in the daring adventure. Setting off from Vauxhall Gardens on November 7, 1833, they moved over the English Channel with an eastward wind. A 2000 foot rope dragging over the forests and the streams kept the balloon level. Eighteen hours later they reached a point in Germany 500 miles away. The three aeronauts landed safely in Weilberg, a town in the Duchy of Nassau.

The excitement over Green's exploit led to the formation of the European Aeronautical Society in London. It was the first company established for air travel. The members constructed the "first aeriel ship," the Eagle—160 feet long, 50 feet high, 40 feet wide—manned by a crew of 17—to establish direct communication between the several capitals of Europe. It had a paddle propulsion system. It had Cayley's cylindrical shape, but Cayley was never consulted. It was exhibited but never flown, since not even seventeen rowers could paddle the ship against the wind. Had they consulted Cayley, or even read his work, they would never have attempted such a means of propulsion. Cayley was to find all through his life that no one really grasped his aerodynamic principles—the fate of a man born before his time.

The balloon resumed its role as a spectacle at fairs. Even Charles Green, after his "finest hour," had to perform mere ascensions before crowds in different cities. Ballooning became a kind of vaudeville of the air—the prime event on every gala occasion. Acrobats performed on dangling trapezes. Hippodrome "girls of the air" froze into the graceful poses of ballerinas before cardboard clouds. Fifty years after Franklin's dream of aerial transport, the balloon had become a loudly painted hussy entertaining the mob with all sorts of divertissements, supporting scantily dressed chorus girls on horses as they rose in the air.

The image of the heroic long-distance voyager did not come to the fore again until the 1840's. Then Charles Green launched a new sweep of public excitement with his startling announcement that the crossing of the Atlantic Ocean would soon become possible. He demonstrated a model of a steerable balloon in the hall of the Polytechnic Institution, newly founded by George Cayley to popularize science. In sober attire Green wound up a spring that activated a propeller for several minutes. The whirling propeller swung to the horizontal and raised the gas bag to the ceiling.

Royal Gardens, Vauxhall.

ASCENT

OF

THE ROYAL

NASSAU BALLOON

FOR THE

Benefit of the Widow

OF

The late Mr. COCKING,

NEXT WEDNESDAY,

9th AUGUST, 1837.

The Friends and Relations of Mrs. COCKING most respectfully acquaint the Nobility, Gentry, and Public, that the Proprietors of Vauxhall having most kindly granted the Gardens and the use of their Royal Nassau Balloon for the above purpose, and Mr. Green having, also, most generously offered his valuable services, an Ascent will take place Next Wednesday, August 9, when all the Proceeds will be appropriated to the relief of the unfortunate Widow, who is entirely left without the means of support.

Seats in the Car may be secured on application at the Gardens;
Gentlemen, £21.---Ladies, £10 : 10s.

☞ Doors open at HALF-PAST TWO.   Balloon to start at SIX.

Admission, HALF-A-CROWN.

Balne, Printer, 38, Gracechurch Street

Poster announcing an appearance of Charles Green.
Smithsonian Institution.

Both propeller and rudder were on the same spindle and could be adjusted separately to lift and to steer a balloon. On the full size balloon waterproof bags were to be lined up along the trail rope. They could be filled as needed with water from a supply in the basket of the balloon to keep the gas bag on a straight, horizontal path. Green claimed there was a steady eastward current of airflow high up from the United States to Europe. He and two passengers with enough food to last three months would start from New York as soon as preparations were completed.

Music hall jingles were written about him: "The days of railways will be o'er/And steam will be esteemed no more/Is a result foreseen by Charles Green/Who says he can/as a matter of course/With a balloon the Atlantic cross."

Shortly after Green's former backer, Monck Mason, announced that he had invented a speedier mechanism to cross the ocean. He spelled out the technical details in a pamphlet, *Remarks on the Ellipsoidal Balloon Propelled by the Archimedean Screw, Described as the new Aerial Machine.* The two fellow passengers of the Nassau voyage were now competitors to win the transatlantic race.

While the two contenders were hurling pamphlets at the public, there came the stupifying news that a giant airplane had been invented that would circle the globe. In fact, William Samuel Henson had designed and patented a huge airliner of World War II shape, size and proportions, 100 years before it became a reality. The patent called for a monoplane with a wing span of 150 feet. The horizontal stabilizer in the rear was shaped like the tail of a bird and it could be expanded or contracted like a fan and swivelled up and down. The tailpiece included a large vertical rudder to keep the plane balanced while making a turn. There was a tricycle landing gear. A twenty-five horsepower steam engine was to be geared to turn twenty-foot pusher propellers of six blades each.

A massive publicity barrage was launched, including full

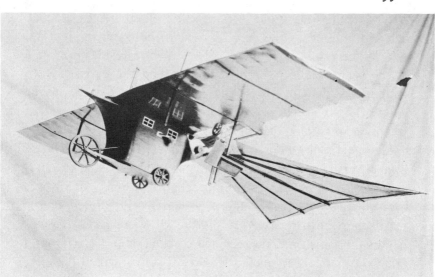

Model of Henson's proposed airliner. *Smithsonian Institution.*

page advertisements, flatly stating that Henson's *Ariel* could "fly to China in twenty-four hours certain." This was astounding news in a day when it took a year to send a letter and receive a reply in London from the farthest point of the British Empire. Stock was sold by public subscription, and Parliament was petitioned to help launch the new sensational air steamer.

When Parliament declined to back the project, Henson organized the Ariel Transit Company to sweep the public into buying shares. The design of *Ariel* was stamped on handkerchiefs, boxes and flags. Rumors were planted in the press that it had crossed the English Channel.

For the public *Ariel* seemed to dwarf the puny balloons that were being readied to race across the Atlantic, since it would have the fantastic speed of 100 miles an hour. The claims of Henson, at first, did not seem to be brazen falsehood. Only a few years before a schoolmaster by the name of Pocock had built two giant kites, each with 100 square feet of surface.

After hitching the flying kites to a horseless carriage, Pocock perched himself on the carriage seat to hold the reins of his two "governable parachutes." The kites, carried aloft by a strong wind in the right direction, pulled the carriage with such speed, they overtook the London Mail Coach on the King's Highway. It was a foretaste of an air speed that promised to surpass that of the railroads.

George Cayley himself was stirred by all this excitement. When he read all the "full particulars" of the *Ariel* in the *Arts and Science Journal*, he realized that Henson's patent was based on his own ideas, which he had freely offered to the world more than thirty years before in *Nicholson's Journal*. About the same time, he received a remarkable letter from a young American engineer, Robert Taylor, which was far more disturbing to him.

The letter described a design for a new kind of aerial carriage. Taylor had projected two four-bladed rotors, moving in opposite directions, to lift a machine vertically in the air. The propellers, one below the other, would be powered by a six horsepower electro-magnetic engine and made to rotate through a double shaft in the hollow of a pipe. The top blades would rotate at a ten degree angle. The lower blades could be inclined by the pilot to up to forty-five degrees by means of wires. Most remarkable of all, after the machine was lifted the pilot could make the two sets of blades close up to create a large plane surface like an immense umbrella. The pilot could then have his machine move forward by a two-bladed propeller in the rear.

The unknown inventor saluted the venerable man of seventy as the originator of the concept "that a large plane surface could attain and retain altitude." But the young man was going to patent his own idea of using propellers for rotary motion on the vertical climb and, when interlocked, to be used as airplane wings. Cayley's flappers he thought were less valuable than the rotating principle of propellers. "Only by the use of rotary motion can we outstrip nature in speed and excel her in endurance."

It was a staggering letter to Cayley because the young man had hit upon an original idea for closing the vanes of a propeller to make a large surface. Cayley felt himself threatened on all sides. Youth was pushing ahead in the thirty-five-year-old Henson, the American engineer of twenty-two, and even his own grandson of twenty-one who was building an ornithopter. Even Green and Mason were using his ideas of a cylindrical shape for their gas bags and swivelling propellers.

After learning that no patent for Taylor's aerial carriage existed, Cayley rushed to design and patent an aerial carriage himself. His design, far more sophisticated than Taylor's was published in an article in *Mechanics Magazine* in April 1843. In the same article that described the aerial carriage, he pointed out the flaws in Henson's *Ariel*. It would never be able to fly because the 4,500 square feet was too large a surface. Any rudder stress would collapse it. It would be better

Model of Cayley's proposed plane. *Smithsonian Institution.*

to create a three decker, a triplane of 1,500 square foot area, the planes separated by ten feet from each other. Henson's vertical sail plane above the wing would be useless for lateral stability. Even his huge wing did not have the dihedral angle important for lateral stability. The use of a huge ramp to get the plane launched to flying speed would be impractical, involving too great an expense. The twenty-five horsepower steam engine was far too heavy to be carried by fragile cloth wings.

In his article Cayley mentioned that his own aerial steam carriage violated no law of aerodynamics. His article concluded, however, with a plea for a huge dirigible. The time was ripe to build the giant elongated balloon, which he had proposed so many times before. He suggested that the three largest balloons in the world should be placed within one egg-shaped envelope, large enough to support the heavy weight of a steam engine, its water and its fuel. Steam engine power would drive the bag at a velocity approaching the railroad pace.

"I think it a national disgrace, in these enlightened locomotive times not to realise by public subscription, the proper scientific experiments which would secure to this country the glory of being the first to establish the dry navigation of the universal ocean of the terrestrial atmosphere."

Cayley considered it the only realistic approach to a transatlantic voyage, but the public dismissed it as chimerical. They were more excited by Cayley's aerial carriage. The most experienced aeronautic engineer of his time was building a heavier-than-air machine! Four different types of aerial vehicles were about to be launched to conquer the air. The race reached the point of sensational interest. And no one was more fascinated by these world-wide news items than Edgar Allan Poe, who for more than ten years had been writing stories of flying machines.

Transatlantic Voyage

EDGAR ALLAN POE HAS BEEN RIGHTFULLY DESCRIBED AS THE
inventor of science-centered fiction. In one of his tales, *The
Thousand-and-Second Tale of Scheherezade,* he describes
some further adventures of Sindbad, who first piloted the
fabulous roc through the air. With prophetic vision, Poe has
Scheherezade spin out yarns of ocean-going steamships carrying thousands of passengers; railroad coaches traveling 300
miles per hour on fifty-foot wide tracks; voices being transmitted across the earth through the air; machines calculating
and printing answers to problems; light rays that change the
characteristics of time and space as they speed into astronomi-
cal distances. The recital of such absurdities infuriates the Sul-
tan, who punishes Scheherezade for thinking him so gullible a
fool as to believe such nonsense. Today, we cannot help but
honor Poe for conceiving such scientific truths.

It is evident that Poe had a keen grasp of the theories of
science. Perhaps he absorbed them from one of his professors
at the University of Virginia who wrote a novel about a moon
voyage, his characters getting there by means of an antigravity device. Years later, Poe sought to find a more credible

59

way to traverse space. He pondered the fact that Encke's comet over the years kept shortening its orbit. Poe figured that there must be matter in space, however thin, which resisted the movement of the comet and thus forced it ever nearer to the earth in shorter ellipses. He theorized that the atmosphere of the sun must extend to the earth in some attenuated form, a concept which has been proven valid only recently.

On the basis of this theory, he has Hans Phoal of Rotterdam fly to the moon by the use of a gas even lighter than hydrogen. In the book he is the first to describe the agony of a human body in the airless cold of space.

After the story was published, he spoke to some friends of a sequel in which he intended to use a super telescope to describe Hans' adventures on the moon. The idea reached the ears of a journalist, who made use of it soon after in a news dispatch to the *New York Sun* in 1835. The reporter claimed that he had received advance sheets of articles written for the Edinburgh *Journal of Science* by the famous astronomer, John Herschel. The astronomer's twenty-four-foot telescope was supposedly illuminated by a "light-infiltration" of such wonderful power that Herschel had brought the moon within a range of eighty miles. The miraculous telescope, in subsequent dispatches, perceived snow white deer on green mountains netted with golden lace and, most exciting of all, flying creatures that were half-bird and half-human.

When two Yale professors asked to see the original mathematical data "of no interest to newspaper readers," the reporter, Alton Locke, had to confess that he had perpetrated a hoax. It had created an international sensation, bringing a small fortune to the author. However, it dashed Poe's opportunity to write the sequel to his moon voyage—a genuine loss to the world of literature.

About ten years later Poe was not caught napping when the

imminent transatlantic race had been built up in the minds of newspaper readers around the world. His imagination leaped to the writing of a newspaper dispatch and a sensational headline—to perpetrate the balloon hoax of the century. He had a sick wife who needed medical attention, and he had only $4.50 in his pocket. It was no time to think of scruples. He dashed off a story.

The Baltimore Sun, a recently launched newspaper, had an exclusive on his electrifying dispatch The editor rushed it into print in a special Saturday edition. Poe, himself, provided the headline in his opening paragraph:

"The great problem is at length solved. The air, as well as the earth and the ocean, has been subdued by science and will become a common and convenient highway for mankind. The Atlantic has been actually crossed in a balloon."

The extraordinary 3,000-mile air voyage, according to Poe's report, started from London on April 6, and ended on Sullivan's Island near Charleston, South Carolina, on April 9. The mechanism that steered and propelled the Victoria (the name of the dirigible) at forty miles an hour, was invented by Monck Mason, who led the expedition of eight passengers. With professional briskness, Poe copied a pamphlet by Monck Mason to describe the twisted bands of flattened spiral wire that triumphed over the propellers used by Cayley, Green and Henson.

Poe, of course, had had no time to check his scientific data. A narrow, helical screw would simply bore through the air without any propelling power. The author added other details of technical nonsense. He had a hurricane advance, instead of destroy, the fragile balloon. When the hurricane settled down, the balloonists ascended five miles to search for another speedy air current to race them to the American coast. We know today that such a jet current does exist, but it is ten miles up, and moving in the opposite direction.

Poe had his aeronauts in rapture over the space view of the

earth, only 25,000 feet up. Stars could be seen by daylight against the deep black of the sky. His men experienced no sensation of freezing, no difficulty of breathing. Even the particles of ice that encrusted the network of the balloon, destined to doom many Arctic explorers, were simply melted by the heat of the sun the following day. A grapnel gripped the sand of the Carolina coast to cap the triumphal three-day voyage.

The Poe dispatch, with its dazzling writing, was reprinted everywhere. A new era seemed to have opened up for mankind. Everybody came to believe, as Poe did, that the idea of a heavier-than-air machine would wither and die, and the gas bag would grow and flourish as the aerial transport of the future. *The Sun* sold out its Saturday edition and readers could hardly wait for Monday's paper to get further details. However, on Monday *The Sun* announced it had received no further mail and was inclined to believe that "the intelligence was erroneous."

When the famous narrative was exposed as a hoax, Poe replied, "If the *Victoria* did not absolutely accomplish the voyage reported, it would be difficult to assign a reason why she should not have accomplished it." It was a challenge to the aeronauts themselves, and it influenced them to make the Atlantic crossing their next great goal.

Actually, Henson, Green and Mason abandoned their plans for lack of financial backing. However, the idea never really died; the press continued presenting new designs for powered balloons of massive proportions, and daring aeronauts continued to make spectacular, if not precedent-shattering flights.

A debonair young daredevil, Arban, attempted to cross the Alps in 1849. He was lucky enough to find a favorable wind to carry him for eight hours on a sky voyage from Marseilles to Turin, Italy. This unexpected achievement aroused worldwide enthusiasm again. Hosts of readers poured over his fascinating account of the first view from the air of Mont Blanc, which he described as an immense crystal scintillating with millions of spangles. He had opened a bottle of wine to toast the god of the winds and had thrown the empty bottle on Mount Visco below him. At last, Samuel Johnson's prediction that no balloon would rise higher than a mountain was proved wrong.

Intoxicated by the acclaim that followed his triumph, Arban promised to make the balloon a ship of discovery. A month later, he set out from Barcelona to cross the Mediterranean, hoping to sweep across the Sahara into the unknown interior of Africa. The winds gave no answer to what happened to him on this reckless, ill-fated adventure.

Arban's disaster aroused the aeronauts to a renewed attack against the formidable barrier of the wind. This time, there was money enough to build the full-sized dirigible that Cayley had proposed: Henri Giffard had dedicated his fortune to battle the wind with the steam engine. All of Paris was excited when the rich aeronaut with the checkered silk vest and stovepipe hat entered the gondola of his steam dirigible for the first test on September 24, 1852.

Giffard's cigar-shaped bag was 144 feet long and 39 feet across. The aeronaut's quarters dangled below the dirigible in a sort of boatlike structure, slung from a long pole suspended by rigging from the gas bag. Extra care was taken to have the chimney of the steam engine pointed downward and covered with a fine wire gauze to prevent any stray embers from reaching the inflammable hydrogen. From his car, Giffard could swing a large, triangular sail at the end of a pole in the rear, which he hoped would act as a rudder.

After sufficient steam was raised, the eleven-foot blades of the propeller started spinning with a heavy roar. The crowds cheered the great engineer, who was already saluted by the press as "the Fulton of the air." The ropes were released and the dirigible floated up. It moved with the breeze at 6.7 miles per hour from Paris to Trappe, seventeen miles away. Then came the real test, as Giffard attempted to swing the dirigible around for the trip back against the wind. The three horse-power steam engine struggled to push 88,000 cubic feet of gas through the mild breeze. In the tug of war, the engine roared to the limit of its capacity. Giffard saw the horizon swing a little and then stop. The huge gas bag remained stationary and then was pushed backward. The great wall of wind had conquered again.

There was no further aeronautical excitement until 1859, when Wise and La Mountain made a twenty-hour journey from St. Louis to Jefferson County, New York. Their 60,000 cubic foot gas bag shot up two miles and flew as fast as a gale would carry it, averaging fifty miles an hour. After almost twenty hours, it came to a crashing halt. They set a long-distance record of 1,120 miles, as well as a fifty miles per hour speed record at a time when the best locomotives never went beyond forty miles per hour. The exultant press, not knowing how to express such incredible speed, described it as the swiftness of a deer contrasted with that of a donkey.

John la Mountain, exhilarated by his amazing flight, lifted his balloon a few months later into a raging gale. This time, the balloon was swept at a hundred mile an hour clip into the unknown wilds of Canada. Since nothing was heard of him in the following months, he was given up for lost. But after landing, La Mountain had managed to hack a canoe out of a log and ride the rapids of a turbulent stream southward. Starved and frozen, he glimpsed, by sheer good luck, a trapper's cabin, where hunters provided food and shelter to bring him back to health. It took months for him to struggle through the wilderness back to civilization with his incredible story. The hundred mile an hour rate of speed revealed a new, amazing potential speed for air travel.

No one had ever made more careful preparations to cross

the Atlantic than Thaddeus Lowe did in the 1850's. He had never forgotten Poe's vivid description, and he devoted years of his life to make that dream a reality. The long-distance voyage of Wise and La Mountain made the 3,000 mile voyage more feasible than ever. A balloon need only be big enough and fly high enough to meet and be carried along on a steady river in the sky. Finally, in 1858, he found financial backing to construct a balloon nine times larger than the conventional size. Its capacity of 725,000 cubic feet gave it gigantic proportions.

The gondola of the air monster was more the size of a small cabin than a basket. Beneath it was slung a thirty-foot, steam-powered lifeboat with water-tight compartments. Lowe attached a helical screw to the lifeboat, powered by a small steam engine, believing it might be helpful in the ascent. His trailing guide rope stretched to one and a half miles with a lead weight at the end. There was a second propeller in the gondola to be whirled by a clock mechanism to keep the balloon from spinning in a high wind. Every device described by Poe and others was incorporated in the great Lowe balloon.

After the balloon was completed, Lowe discovered that there was not enough hydrogen in New York to fill the monstrous bag. So he transferred it to Philadelphia and named it the *Great Western*. It happened to make its trial flight on the same day that the *Great Eastern* steamship first docked in New York. When the *Great Western* was inflated for the transatlantic crossing on September 8, a high wind suddenly arose and, just as suddenly, the huge balloon bag was ripped apart. The technology of the time had not advanced quite enough for such vaulting ambition.

Undaunted, Lowe built another balloon, this time far smaller in size. He launched it, but as it flew eastward to cross the ocean, the bag proved to be overloaded and managed to be airborne only as far as Connecticut. Even this did not

Inflating *The Great Western* balloon. *Smithsonian Institution.*

stop Lowe, and the following year he flew from Cincinnati
to Pea Ridge, South Carolina, trying to find for himself the
prevailing westerly wind high up. When he landed, he was
imprisoned as a Northern spy, for this was the tense period
just before the Civil War erupted. He was eventually freed,
but only because he met an old friend among the Confederates.

Lowe organized a balloon corps for the Union Army. His
observation balloon was connected with a telegraph wire over
which he detailed Confederate maneuvers under General Lee,
making possible McClellan's victory in the Battle of Fair
Oaks. But the military officials could not see the value of a
tethered balloon; the corps was disbanded. But interest in air
ships remained.

Facts, sometimes, can be less interesting than fantasy. There was the mysterious case of Dr. Andrews. He stirred up not only the world of balloonists, but the general public as well, with his claim that his flying machine, *Aereon*, could master the stiffest winds without a motor. He had built his remarkable "antigravity" ship, he said, to shorten the war against the Confederates.

Abraham Lincoln recommended that the War Department look into it. Interviewed by a general in Washington, Dr. Andrews was asked about the motive power that could prevail against the wind. In short, the general heard the preposterous explanation that the *Aereon*, comprised of three parallel, cigar-shaped bags, was capable of moving against the wind by taking advantage, not of the wind, but the force of gravity. Deeming the explanation technical nonsense, the general stalked out of the room. But there were reputable witnesses to the flight of the *Aereon*—a postmaster, a justice of the peace and New York newspaper reporters. They swore that they had seen the *Aereon* move "faster than lightning," "circle like a bird" and "plunge into an opposing wind with the speed of a cannon ball."

Once again the press proclaimed, "The problem of the centuries has been solved." *The New York Herald* said flatly, "The navigation of the air is a fixed fact." The speed of the *Aereon* was estimated at 120 miles an hour.

Dr. Andrews really believed he had demonstrated motorless, gravitational propulsion. Not since Poe's balloon hoax of April 13, 1844, had there been such mass excitement. When the *Aereon* flew over New York during the Civil War, practically all the 700 stagecoaches rumbling up and down the cobblestone streets had to stop as the passengers rushed out to look skyward. All business stopped. Leaflets fluttered down with the printed promise that a fleet of gravitational balloons could win the war.

And yet the wonder vanished into thin air. A financial

panic after the war wiped out Dr. Andrews. Those who were the first to acclaim him were now disposed to jeer. The *Aereon* vanished into the myths and mists of history. How could reputable persons have said it moved "faster than lightning" against the wind?

Very likely, so little was known about air currents in 1862 that no one realized that the *Aereon* was swung around by the play of thermals. Spirally moving thermal columns of warm air rise hundreds of feet between cold fronts. Some such sport of weather provided the witnesses with the illusion that the *Aereon* high up was moving against the wind, when it was simply being sucked around by a thermal spiral.

In 1844 Poe had had the passengers of his transatlantic balloon enjoying the view from five miles above the earth. They felt no discomfort; the stars against a black sky could be seen by daylight. In 1862 the British Association for the Advancement of Science sent aloft a balloon to investigate this mysterious region. James Glaisher and Henry Tracey Coxwell volunteered to go up five miles and beyond.

The balloon was launched near the gas works of Wolverhampton, England, on September 5, 1862, just about the time Dr. Andrews was startling the crowds of New York. The log of Glaisher and Coxwell seemed to confirm Poe's predictions at first. They felt no suffering of any kind. On the contrary, Glaisher experienced a pervading radiance of light and an inner joy. At 21,000 feet, his mind and body seemed to weaken, but so gradually, so insensibly, he was barely conscious of it. There was a deceptive sense of self-confidence. Breathing had become difficult, but there was no suspicion of any danger. It seemed only amusing that the slightest exertion on his part resulted in his panting like a dog that had run too fast. It was strange that he felt no desire to move his arms or legs. Stranger still was the throbbing of his heart. He recalled that he was not alarmed even when it pounded so hard as to shake his body. The false euphoria lasted until the danger line was reached, thirty seconds before unconsciousness.

Just before the danger point, Glaisher noted that his companion's face had turned a bronze color. This shocked him into action. He decided to lower the balloon. To his horror, he discovered that his fingers were so numb he could not clutch the cord for the release of gas. With a convulsive effort, he managed to seize the valve cord with his teeth, seconds before he fell backward into a faint. Fortunately, he had opened the valve and the balloon lowered itself to the level where life-giving oxygen revived the prostrate aeronauts.

The written account of this highest voyage so alarmed the world of aeronautics, that another serious ascension was not made until twenty-five years later. It was a discouraging record. Not a single balloon had been built capable of making a long-distance voyage of exploration. The balloon had really not changed since Charles first invented the light wicker basket, its network suspension, the varnished silk bag, and its valve on top. Balloons were still completely at the mercy of the wind. It was a stalemate that led others to think that the heavier-than-air machine, after all, might prove to be more important than balloons. Progress there had been equally slow.

The Father of
Aerial Navigation

HENSON, DESIGNER OF THE 150 FOOT *Ariel*, WAS AT THE END
of his tether by 1847. He had no money to build his machine
and was no longer sure it would work if he did build it. Cayley's article had discouraged him. He wrote a flattering letter
to Cayley, honoring him as "the father of aerial navigation."
The letter amounted to a confession that Henson and Stringfellow needed the help of the master, who had devoted a lifetime to the mathematical measurements of aerodynamics.

But Cayley was equally baffled by the need for an engine,
without which no aircraft could become practical. He could
only reply, regretfully, that if he were shown "any experimental proof of mechanical flight, maintainable for a sufficient
time by mechanical power," he would be glad to join their
enterprise.

Henson abandoned all hope and sailed for America with his
bride. He was never to know that his design of *Ariel* would
have a major influence in the world of early twentieth century aviation. A certain measure of immortality would come
to him long after he died in Texas in 1891.

The year after Henson left for America, John Stringfellow

completed an engine-driven model of an airplane. His one-
cylinder steam engine had a weight-power ratio of 13 to 1,
making it the most efficient steam engine of its time. It
powered twin propellers in the rear of the car, whirling them
at six times the engine speed. To test the model, he suspended
it on a sixty-foot-wire and flew the length of a long room in
Stringfellow's lace factory. The best that could be said of it—
that it had "a tendency to lift"—was not enough to encourage
him to continue.

Accounts of Stringfellow's valiant efforts to fly a powered
model must have made an impression on the father of aerial
navigation. For immediately after, Cayley resumed experiments. In his 1809 article, Cayley had boasted, "I shall construct a very useful engine of the flight of a single person by
muscular strength in the course of a little time." The "little
time" had extended to forty-four years in 1849. He was
seventy-nine years old, but he felt a new compulsion to vindicate his lifetime of labor. This time, he permitted nothing to
distract him from his goal.

It seemed to him that no one had really understood his
fundamentals of aerodynamics. There was no real compre-
hension of the delicate forces that moved about the vertical
axis of a flying machine—rolling, pitching, yawing—that could
be stabilized and controlled only by precise mathematical
measurements. The hope of an airborne future rested on
Cayley, alone. He would have to demonstrate a manned flight,
before aeronauts could be stirred to study his principles more
carefully.

To build a man-carrying machine, he resumed experiments
with large size airfoils on a new swinging arm test rig. As
always, he realized the need to gather fundamental data before embarking on a new construction. He calculated that his
machine would need 500 square feet of surface, capable of
carrying a pound for every square foot. He built a smaller
triplane glider in 1849, but he did not complete his full-size

A drawing from Cayley's Notebook.

machine until 1853.

This time he fixed the car to the wings with struts and diagonal bracing. It was the first time diagonal bracing was used to insure the sturdiness of the wings so they could carry a heavier load.

To secure better stability, he built separate tailpieces for the car and the wings. The larger tailpiece was placed in back of the wings and tilted at a slightly elevated angle to prevent the glider from pitching should it be exposed to a sudden gust of wind. The smaller tailpiece was connected to the back of the car. A movable rudder was to be swung by the pilot for steering, by means of a rope and tiller. At the same time a separate horizontal surface below the rudder could be made to rise or descend as might be needed.

While putting the finishing touches to his glider, Cayley received a request from Paris to provide material for a new magazine, launched in support of heavier-than-air craft. Heartened by this new revival of interest, Cayley mailed his designs and detailed explanations to the French *Bulletin*. The

French editor arranged to publish them in installments.

Only one part of Cayley's summation was published, describing the mechanism he was using to flap the wings. The *Bulletin* went bankrupt before the full analysis and the all-important design was published. The future aeronauts of France would have been spared many tragic blunders if they had had Cayley's complete and illustrated design. As a result, only a limited portion of Cayley's illuminating discoveries in aerodynamics trickled down to later generations.

By 1853 Cayley had designed his manned glider so carefully that the total drag, he figured, was only 1/16th of its weight. He was pleased with what his mechanics had accomplished with his precise specifications. One could almost hear his sigh when he wrote in his notebook that if the explosion engine were perfected, "aerial navigation would be at our command without further delay."

He was so confident of its inherent stability, he would have piloted it himself, if he had not been burdened with his eighty years. As it was, with the greatest difficulty, he persuaded his coachman to try it out. Cayley had the reluctant coachman practice launching the wheeled aerial carriage, unmanned, over the valley to prove its safety and stability. The coachman was asked to practice "rowing" while the glider was in a resting position so as to feel the lift with each push and pull of his arms. In this way, the coachman, finally, built up enough courage to launch himself into the unsubstantial air.

The open space within the wheeled glider made it possible for him to run with it for flying speed over the hill. Then he lifted himself on the perch, where he rowed the levers as if his life depended on it. The flapping sails carried the glider across the valley to the other side, landing at a point far beyond any it had reached before. The momentum carried the wheels even further, stopping, finally, without a jolt.

The coachman emerged, white and exhausted, to await the jubilantly yelling group that ran towards him.

This flying man was no Victorin. He did not experience the feeling of ecstasy that might be expected of a man that had flown like a bird successfully for the first time in history. He was too frightened, too shaken by the experience. He felt he had had a narrow escape from death. The congratulations of his master meant nothing to him. "Please, Sir George, I wish to give notice. I was hired to drive and not to fly." He feared most of all he might be persuaded to do it again.

History knows very little of this historic flight or the glider. Nothing remained except the notes of George Cayley, resurrected from an attic trunk only a few years ago. A nine-year-old child remembered it vaguely and spoke of it towards the end of her long life. This we know—the first heavier-than-air flight did not generate the excitement of that of a *Montgolfière* or a *Charlière*. There were no reporters on the scene. Half of London did not come to see the miracle. Cayley pushed the matter no further. "I have a hatred of puffing," he said. It was sufficient for him that he had fulfilled the boast of his youth. He had seen the future, and he was at peace with himself. He was certain that the future would apply the laws of mechanics to the air ocean and make it navigable.

He was not so sure the next year. A French aeronaut, M. Letur, devised a glider parachute apparatus without having absorbed Cayley's knowledge. A balloon 1,000 feet over Cremarne Gardens in London released Letur. He circled like a bird as he descended, but at the last moment he lost control and was hurled against some trees, to be fatally injured. The

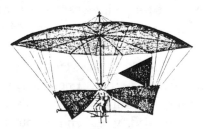

The glider parachute of M. Letur.

knowledge of how to fly was there, but no one seemed willing to use it.

When Cayley died in 1857, he was so modest a man that the inscription on his tombstone, by his order, read "When I am gone there will not be a friend wanted." We know today the contrary was true. Such a friend of aeronautics was not to come again until the next century. The verdict of history is that aviation would have advanced fifty years if Cayley's writings had reached a wide enough audience. Gliding would have been taken up everywhere and engineers would have been encouraged to perfect the internal combustion engine. As it was, the great Cayley lacked a great audience. A flying plane was not to arouse the public until 1910—a hundred years after Cayley had spelled out all the fundamental principles.

Cayley's theoretical writings were basic, but they were read in garbled and abbreviated versions by the aeronauts who came after him. In 1853 Jean Marie Le Bris, a retired sea captain, must have read Cayley's article in the French *Bulletin*. He learned only about flapping wings. He had no concept of the subtle mathematics of pressures one was required to know to build a glider of inherent stability.

Legend has it that Le Bris, during a lifetime of voyaging, fell in love with the albatross, the romantic bird that flies indefinitely without flapping, in an easy, effortless glide. Those who have sailed the Pacific know the albatross as a constant companion aboard a ship. Le Bris became fascinated when he observed how the bird hopped and ran along the deck of his ship with outstretched wings to build up momentum to soar. He became obsessed with the desire to build a mechanical duplicate of this sea bird with bamboo strips and linen.

When he retired to a farm in Brittany, he was heartened to learn that an Englishman had built a full-size mechanical bird with flapping wings in 1853. Le Bris did not have Cayley's mathematical training, so he decided to make a flying

Le Bris' flying machine.

machine in proportion to an albatross. Each wing had a spread of twenty-three feet. The wings of light ash were covered with flannel and stressed with wires. He created a system of cords, pulleys and tillers, supposed to make the wings flap. He added a tail with hinges so that he could move it up or down and sideways like a rudder. He christened it the *Albatross* and decided to risk his life without first testing it in the air as a kite.

After hitching his flyer on the top of a horse-drawn wagon, he sat with ropes in his hands for the necessary steering. He signaled the driver of the cart to gallop the horses down a hill road at top speed. Sweeping down the steep hillside in the face of a twelve-mile-wind, the mechanical bird unexpectedly lifted off the wagon and suddenly soared to a height of thirty feet.

A rope, dangling from the machine, became entangled around the body of the driver, jerking him off his seat. The frightened man clutched frantically at the rope and found himself dangling in the air and soaring over a valley below him. Le Bris heard his howls and, though equally scared, had wit enough to pull the rope that lifted the tail and let the glider swoop down to the valley below. Le Bris then swung the rudder to the left to reach a cleared field. Miraculously, driver, pilot and glider landed—shaken up, but intact. Without realizing it, the dangling driver had kept the *Albatross* on a balanced course as it zoomed down to an easy gliding landing —a perfect adjustment of the center of gravity to the center of support.

Elated, Le Bris attempted a second flight, this time over a quarry. He took care not to entangle the driver with his release rope. Without the balance of a suspended weight, the *Albatross* was smashed and Le Bris broke his leg.

After his recovery, the fascinated townspeople pleaded with him to continue his experiments, offering to finance him. A new, mechanical bird was built, but Le Bris refused to take any more chances. This time, he used his glider as a kite with a long string line. It rose to 600 feet and dashed down to be destroyed on the ground.

Le Bris never flew again. He realized there were forces in the air, laws of aerodynamics, which he did not understand and over which he had no control. Le Bris never put his experiences in writing and left only a legend behind him. However, the dangling man did inspire the idea of a fixed-wing glider, with a man dangling from it to control it by shifting his weight. Louis-Pierre Mouillard, a retired sea captain like Le Bris, devoted the leisure hours on his farm in Algiers to building such a fixed-wing glider. For reasons of safety, he made the wings only breast high and raced down a hill with his contraption. He found himself soaring over a ditch, his wings sailing upon the wind. Frightened, he tried to get down to the ground, but was unable to do so until his glider, with a will of its own, it seemed, slid down gradually to the ground.

This unexpected success made gliding his consuming passion. The spell of the birdman was upon him for the rest of his life. He built many gliders and wrote a popular book, *The Empire of the Air*, about his experiences. One sentence in the book cast its spell upon others:

"I hold that in the flight of the soaring birds (the vultures, the eagles, and other birds which fly without flapping) ascension is produced by a skillful use of the force of the wind, and the steering, in any direction, is the result of skillful maneuvers, so that in a moderate wind a man can, with an aeroplane, unprovided with any motor whatever, rise into the air and direct himself at will, even against the wind, itself."

While Le Bris was testing his *Albatross*, another French naval officer, Felix Du Temple (1823-1890), read a French translation of Cayley with deeper insight than any one else had. He built a model of an airplane, powered by clockwork, that took off under its own power, sustained itself, and landed safely. Historians call it the first authentic flight of a powered model. Two years after Cayley's death, one of Cayley's followers seemed at last to have understood his work. But a life-size edition of the model, built ten years later, did not achieve the stability hoped for. Another gallant attempt ended in failure. What was lacking was the genius of George Cayley.

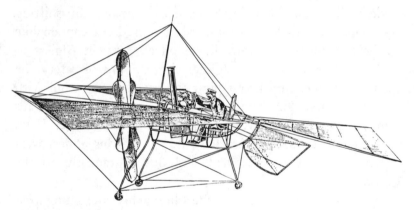

The flying machine of Felix de Temple, 1874.

The Amateur Inventor

IN THE NEXT FEW DECADES FLYING MACHINES AND BALLOONS seesawed in prominence. The public, of course, was more intrigued by the spectacle of balloons with which they had become familiar. Any daring exploit by a balloonist aroused tremendous enthusiasm. Aware of the public pulse, a young playwright of thirty-three chose the history of ballooning as the subject of his first book. His name was Jules Verne.

It was a choice that bewildered his friends. Verne had concocted twenty machine-made plays for the Paris stage. He was on the verge of theatrical success. Why change horses in midstream?

The truth was that Jules Verne had been leading a double life. Unknown to his friends, the young dramatist had snatched odd hours in the Bibliotheque Nationale to feed a secret passion for exploration and science. For more than ten years, he had been jotting down strange and stunning scientific facts that he had filed away in notebooks in separate drawers of his desk.

What amazed and delighted him in his years of research was that the most far-reaching inventions were made by the simplest means. Simply by dissolving iron filings in dilute sulphuric acid, a new gas was created that brought in the world of ballooning. Nothing could be simpler than the zinc and iron plates that Volta piled up in a solution of brine to produce a steady flow of electricity. A man like Faraday needed only a magnet, a few wires and some bits of iron and copper to discover the laws of electromagnetism, which soon after caused telegraphs to be strung over the landscape of continents.

Even more startling, Verne learned that many great inventions were made by amateurs. By profession, Franklin was a printer; Montgolfier, a paper manufacturer; Fulton and Morse, portrait painters. Whittling boys brought up on farms worked out, by trial and error, the mechanical reaper, the sewing machine, the cotton gin that removed the burden of back-breaking labor from housewives and farmers. Here were benefits beyond the ability of generals and politicians to perform, yet made by simple workers who were not specialists.

In addition, all of Verne's plays had been commercial failures; it seemed to him he had wasted his time. A fortunate marriage and the easy hours of a stockbroker made it possible for him to concentrate his scattered energies on writing a history of ballooning.

He had discovered that science with its theories led you by the hand to the very door of invention. In back of his mind was the hope of inventing a new mechanism for a balloon. After learning all about aerostatics while researching his history, he might be in a position to invent a new propulsion system.

For the last chapter of his history, the dramatist in Verne took over. Charles Green had claimed that he could stay up in the air for three months with his new guide rope and swivelling propeller whirled by a clock mechanism, but there had been no financial backers. An exciting idea had come into

Verne's imagination. He would create the first transcontinental balloon, just as Poe had imagined the transoceanic, steerable *Victoria*. He would create a character like Charles Green to build a balloon capable of exploring Africa and discovering the source of the Nile.

In the early 1860's, Austria, England and France had all sent out expeditions to penetrate that part of "dark Africa" that was blanked out white on maps in geography books. All three exploring safaris had entered the unknown jungle the year before, but no news had come back. The slightest dispatch about them would have made headlines in the world press as big as any of the battles of the American Civil War. The silence was ominous.

Verne's extensive research in the history of geography had made him an authority on African exploration. Of the 130 known explorers, only a handful had returned to give accounts of horrifying ordeals. The steaming jungle floor of Africa had an odor of decay and death. Explorers were struck down by fevers and disease, devoured by cannibals and crocodiles, tortured by witch doctors, captured as slaves by Moors, or put to death by natives as tribal drums throbbed their menacing beat. Those who managed to escape and come back were emaciated, disease-ridden, shadows of their former selves. Central Africa had become known as the "White Man's Graveyard."

Instead of a nightmare, a balloon exploration might be a delightful excursion. As Verne wrote:

"If I come to a mountain, I fly over it; a precipice, I cross it; a storm, I rise over it; a torrent, I skim over it like a bird. I travel without fatigue and halt without need of rest . . . with the map of Africa unwinding below my eyes in the greatest atlas of the world."

Like all inventions, Verne's imaginary balloon, the *Victoria*, developed in a series of stages. Imagination was not enough to dream up an authentic new invention. The total conception must be made up of engineering details that had precision and obeyed the laws of science.

He had grasped the central problem of a long-distance balloon voyage—the constant diminishment of gas. There was too frequent a need to open the valve on top to lower the gas bag. The mile-long trailing guide rope of Charles Green to keep the balloon at a steady altitude was too damaging to property and persons on the ground. One lad had been killed. Green's propeller required too much muscular exertion. The time was ripe to find still another way to save gas.

"It is no longer a question of directing the course of a balloon so much as it is a question of moving up and down without losing gas, which is the strength, the blood, the soul, so to speak, of the balloon."

Verne's aerial explorer would require frequent up and down movements as he searched out the source of the Nile. Near the surface, the great trade winds collided with hills and mountains, which are like reefs in a river bed. The air masses are swept into turbulence. Valleys and mountains change not only the force, but the very direction of the wind.

In short, winds could be moving in different directions at different levels. Verne asked himself how he could get a balloon to go up and down to search out the wind current that had the direction he needed. Researching on this control idea, he learned that hydrogen expands 1/480th of its own volume with every degree of heat. As it ascends towards the sun, the temperature of the gas doubles every three miles. At the start of ascent, a full balloon would be sure to burst. A half-filled balloon was necessary for control.

Verne recalled Meusnier's suggestion that an air bag within an outer envelope could preserve the shape of the balloon, making it more buoyant. Verne went one step further. Why not fill both bags with hydrogen and connect the two? The bag-within-a-bag concept could permit a flow of hydrogen between them as the gas contracted or expanded with a lower or higher temperature. How much simpler and more efficient to have a balloon rise and fall by the heating and the cooling of the gas than to force such movements by mechanical propellers, which required constant muscular power.

The technical question that followed was to figure out the kind of heating apparatus that would have little weight and high temperature. Verne recalled a recent invention of Goldsworthy Gurney, the man who had created steam carriages in Britain. Gurney combined the combustion of oxygen and hydrogen to make a blowtorch, which produced so hot a flame it could melt all metals except platinum. The hydrogen within the gas bag would respond in seconds to such a flame.

The apparatus worked itself out in his imagination: a pipe could extend down from the outer bag into the gondola of a large balloon, where it would be coiled within a cylinder and extend up again into the inner bag. The blowtorch need simply lick a projecting platinum head outside the cylinder, starting a circulating movement of the gas. Simply by applying and withdrawing the flame, the gas could be instantly heated or cooled. Certainly, the heating apparatus of connecting tubes, a cylinder and a blowpipe would have far less weight and be more effective than the clumsy steam engines and clock mechanisms of previous inventors.

Like all inventors, Verne solved one problem to find another looming up. How could he replenish the oxygen and hydrogen gases within the blowpipe? He would have to use a bank of lead-acid batteries to decompose water into its elements. That meant the extra weight of batteries and a series of containers for the water and the resulting gases. With the help of his brother-in-law, who was a professor of mathematics, Verne worked out the size of the balloon to take care of the weight factor.

The oxygen at one end of the water chest could escape into a second chest. At the negative pole, the hydrogen could bubble up into a third container. He figured out that the fourth chest, mixing the two gases, would have to be about forty cubic feet. This fourth chest would be connected to the blowtorch by means of a stopcock. Since he could always replenish the twenty-five gallon chest of water, for water was to found everywhere, his balloon journey, no matter how long, would thus have its steady supply of gases.

We would call such an invention today a Rube Goldberg contraption, but in Verne's mind, a hundred years ago, everything seemed to fit. It violated no laws of science. He could ascend by heating. He could descend by removing the heat. A quick, upward movement was possible to escape danger beneath or surmount looming obstructions ahead. After adding up the weights of all the items, Verne found to his joy that he need use only a moderate-sized balloon.

Once his problems were worked out, he went to work on the last chapter of his history. Soon the book was completed. But Verne faced bitter disappointment. Over a period of a year every publisher in Paris turned down his history.

While Jules Verne was churning out his ideas for a transcontinental balloon, a Monsieur Tournachon had become enamoured of the potential of the heavier-than-air machine. There had been many small advances. Felix Du Temple had launched a powered model of an airplane into the air. Ponton d'Amercourt had just put a new helicopter toy on the market. It was driven by clockworks, and it had a miniature parachute to bring it back gently to earth. Lenoir had just invented the explosion engine. Inflammable coal gas was mixed with air and compressed within a cylinder by means of a piston. An electric spark set off an explosion behind each stroke of the piston with enough force to raise 550 pounds a foot per second. In aeronautic terms, this was equivalent to the force exerted by six men to turn a propeller, but with the lightness of weight of a single man.

Monsieur Tournachon was famous in France under the name Nadar, as the most popular caricaturist of Paris, the author of five novels and the most sensational photographer of his time. He had applied the illumination of the new electric arc to photography, enabling him to take the first pictures of the sewers and catacombs of the city. Then he made numerous ascents in balloons to photograph the first aerial views.

Aerial photography was no easy matter in those days. Nadar had to drag up equipment weighing more than a hundred pounds and a trip on a balloon was not as serene as it might look to an observer below. Hydrogen can expand with frightening swiftness on a warm day, and up shoots the gas bag. A cloud passes overhead and down you go. Throw out a handful of sand and up you soar. Meet a cold downdraft and you might be sucked down at sixty miles an hour to hit the ground with a bang. Such choppy ups and downs were certainly no comfortable perch from which to take a photograph. Such experiences had soured Nadar on the subject of balloons and made the possibility of a heavier-than-air machine sound exciting to him.

Nadar found himself pursuing aeronautics with the passion of a hound who has the scent of a hare. A model of a powered airplane had flown. A toy helicopter had risen and made a soft landing. A new explosion engine had been patented. Why was nothing further being done about it? He discovered the writings of Cayley. Nadar was no engineer nor mathematician, but he was a poet who recognized the accents of truth in the words of Cayley. Only the want of an engine, Cayley had written, held back the practical airplane, and it was a "national disgrace" that the government did nothing about it.

The words set off an explosion in Nadar, who had the crusading spirit of a reformer. In fact, he became the most articulate spokesman for the heavier-than-air machine. Nadar decided to organize a society dedicated to driving ballooning out of business. It had a long name: The International Society for the Encouragement of Aerial Locomotion by Means of Apparatus Heavier than Air. The Society put out a new magazine, *L'Aeronaute*, that featured on its front cover a design by Gabriel de la Landelle of a "Stream Airliner." The boat-shaped body had two monoplane wings and rudder-elevator assemblies fore and aft. Instead of ship's masts, the design illustrated two tall helicopter vanes to be whirled by steam power. Above the vanes, two umbrella parachutes were mounted to be carried folded and opened only during emergencies.

Nadar himself wrote the manifesto on *L'autolocomotion aérienne*. The balloon, he thundered was the principal obstruction to the development of proper flying. He taunted the

Drawing of de la Landelle's flying machine.

balloonists, who were given the honorable title "professor" by the press; let them deserve the title by creating a steerable balloon. Everyone knew that a balloon was born a buoy and would ultimately burst as a mere buoy. An object must be heavier than air to command the air. The future of the air lay with mechanics.

The ghost of Cayley had found, at last, an eloquent voice. Unfortunately, Nadar did not realize that Cayley's aerial carriage of 1843 was pure gold. Years later, the Smithsonian Institution was to make a model of Cayley's design and find that with a suitable engine, it could be lifted and flown. Instead, Nadar chose Landelle's design—*l'aeromotive*—and used it as a model for the future. The most eloquent spokesman for Cayley did not understand aerodynamics and chose the wrong helicopter.

The voice of the indefatigable Nadar was heard on lecture platforms everywhere. He cried out that good will and intelligence ought to organize themselves as a sacred duty to transform the conditions of life. Of what use was the most learned legislator of France if he had no vision? He was robbing the young of their enthusiasm for the future. Without dreams, there can be no progress. Future inventions should become a serious and responsible public business.

To those who argued with him that man would need a wing span of 12,000 square feet to enable him to soar (quoting the eighteenth century physicist Coulombier), Nadar used illustrations from nature that he had gleaned from Cayley. A turkey buzzard, weighing five pounds, flies with a wing span of six feet; a man, weighing 150 pounds, should be able to fly with a wing span of 180 feet. One pound of goose feathers can pick up nineteen pounds of goose and carry it at half a mile a minute. If a goose can do it, certainly man should be able to surpass it. Man should rely on speed to reduce his weight in the air, just as a fast skater manages to hurl himself over thin ice without breaking through. Only lack of sufficient knowledge held man back. But all Nadar's eloquence could not raise the funds he needed until he met Jules Verne.

By the time Verne and Nadar met, Verne had become so disillusioned with his book on the history of ballooning, he was glad to join a society intended to eliminate balloons. The two men met after a meeting of the society, seated opposite each other at a cafe table.

Nadar was furious at the laughter he had provoked at the meeting when he claimed in a speech that his "aeromotive" would travel from Paris to London in two hours. Jules Verne, with equal vehemence, expressed his own anger that no publisher in Paris believed that his projected balloon would be able to cross Africa in five weeks.

Nadar, of course, was startled and intrigued with the rash statement of his dramatist friend—and dared him to prove it. Verne went into a detailed explanation of his new invention. But his mechanism would remain only a vain dream, Verne concluded sadly. Publishers were convinced there was no market for a book on balloons; the age of aeronautic heroes was finished. The carnival ascents of aeronauts had become as safe and unglamorous as any routine railroad trip.

To Verne's surprise, the idea of his compensating balloon struck Nadar with the force of an explosion. Nadar gnawed his nails feverishly as a new vision expanded before his mind. If the expensive hydrogen gas could be saved, as Verne claimed, then a gigantic balloon would be a cheap and splendid way to gather funds to build his "aeromotive." Entire populations of cities would pay a franc apiece to see the greatest giant of the sky ascending. It could become a spectacle in every large city of Europe and collect enormous profits.

Nadar was talking of millions of francs until Verne impatiently interrupted with his plaint that his book could not even get a 300 franc advance from a publisher. Nadar suddenly recalled that a friend was about to branch out from comic magazines to books for young readers. Then and there, in the cafe, Nadar called for pen and ink and wrote out a letter of introduction to the publisher, Hetzel, for Verne.

Hetzel turned out to be a publisher of genius. He wanted no dry-as-dust history of ballooning. He was searching for writers who could bring the magic of adventurous narrative to fact books. He felt certain such books would be devoured by children who were starved for fantasy. Hetzel persuaded the young dramatist and historian to combine his two talents and make a thriller out of his last chapter. All the information that Verne had accumulated could be inserted as part of the narrative, like raisins in a pudding.

The idea set off an inner storm in Verne's mind which, like the drawers of his desk, had been split into two separate departments; in one, ideas for dramatic plots; in the other, startling facts about science and exploration. Hetzel proved to be the catalyst who churned the contents of these two separate drawers together. As a result, Verne hit upon the formula for a new kind of science fiction book.

What followed was an explosion of energy rare in the history of literature. *Five Weeks in a Balloon* was completed in two weeks. It was a mad dash of writing that compressed breathtaking adventure, the history of ballooning and the history of African exploration into 50,000 words. Overwhelmed, Hetzel gladly paid 10,000 francs for the story and guaranteed Verne 20,000 francs a year in a twenty-year contract for forty such books.

The Giant Balloon

VERNE BEGINS *Five Weeks in a Balloon* WITH DR. FERGUSSON, a friend, and his faithful Negro companion, Joe, starting off in his balloon, the *Victoria*, from Zanzibar on the Indian Ocean to take advantage of the constant trade winds blowing east to west below the equator. The plan is to follow the trail of the Burton-Speke expedition, which had been head-lines in the world press two years before. The caravan had taken four dreadful months to cross a miasmic jungle. Verne has his *Victoria* traverse the same route in two days. The swampy flatland simply unrolls itself at their feet like a beautiful green dream. They feel nothing of the slimy mud, the suffocating, steamy air, the painful stings of insects. The aeronauts had merely to light their blowtorch to skip over a looming mountain. Towards evening, they throw out their grapnel to fasten their balloon to the branches of an enormous Indian fig tree.

From then on, however, the mishaps of adventure pile up at an alarming rate. They shoot up through an electrical storm and rise above the convulsions to a serene and starry heaven. They spy a krall, a village of giant mushroom-shaped

The *Victoria* escapes from a native village—from
an early American edition of Verne's book.

huts hidden among tropical trees. After descending, they find
themselves worshipped as moon gods until a genuine, full
moon rises in the night sky. They escape the angry natives
only by the quick use of their heating invention. The miraculous balloon evades disasters and enemies by vaulting, swoop-
ing and zooming through the jungle.

The aeronauts reach inland lakes and discover the source
of the Nile at a point not yet reached by the struggling, har-
assed European expeditions, and so claim the victory with

appropriate ceremonies. From the safety of his balloon, the hero observes and comments on native tribes in combat and expresses his disgust for such bloody butchery. He rescues a missionary from torture by overawing the natives by the brilliance of an arc light, contrived with two carbon sticks connected to the batteries.

Shifting winds carry the balloon to the Sudan, the delta of the Niger and to the lower Senegal rivers, parts of Africa unexplored until then. They are becalmed in a desert and nearly die of thirst, when a monsoon, in the nick of time, lifts them from their sweltering pit. The outer envelope of their balloon is destroyed by the teeth and claws of vultures, but their inner bag enables them to continue their journey. They survive a vast cloud of locusts, showers of arrows from native tribes, flaming squibs attached to flocks of pigeons, that are let loose upon them to ignite their balloon.

Disaster threatens when the balloon's covering begins to disintegrate under the tropical sun. As they lose gas, Joe saves the buoyancy of the balloon by jumping overboard into a lake. The aeronauts search for him in the Lake Tchad area and days later find him racing a horse to escape from pursuing Arabs. The balloonists release their silken rope ladder and, as quick-witted Joe grasps the ladder, they throw out 150 pounds of ballast. The balloon and dangling Joe are suddenly lifted far above the heads of the enraged pursuers.

The Arab horsemen continue to follow the balloon which, they see, is rapidly losing gas. Everything has to be jettisoned, including the basket, itself. They manage to reach the Senegal river, when, all gas gone, the balloon becomes an empty bag on a tree top. The resourceful explorers hastily gather a huge mound of dried grass, burn it and transform the *Victoria* into a *Montgolfière*, lifted by hot air. It carries them, clinging to the ropes, above the vengeful heads of the savage horsemen, floating them safely across the river into the welcoming hands of French troops.

Joe escapes from Arab horsemen—
from an early American edition of Verne's book.

Never before had there been such an exciting balloon journey. The heating apparatus of the *Victoria* seemed to millions
of readers the next logical step in the mechanical evolution
of balloons. The transcontinental aerial voyage gave the impression of reportage rather than fantasy, and made the story
seem as real as tomorrow's headlines.

The whole world had been waiting anxiously for news of
the lost expeditions that had disappeared in the heart of
Africa. Verne's aerial feat thus became the fulfillment of a

universal dream. The technical details, the sober factual account, the precise mathematics suspended all disbelief. No one read it as fiction. It was a history of the near future. The *Victoria* was as scientific a marvel for Verne's day as the latest spacecraft is for us.

Published on New Year's day of 1863, it became more of a sensational success than even the publisher anticipated. When Nadar advertised his plan to build the largest balloon in the world to make a reality of Verne's novel, a wave of patriotism swept the nation. France would become the Queen of the Air as Britain was the Mistress of the Sea. The bond issue of 200,000 francs was oversubscribed. Hard-headed investors never doubted that Nadar's *Giant* would follow Verne's *Victoria* across the continents and the seas.

At a press conference Nadar explained the compensating mechanism on which he based his confidence. "I shall dispose under the monster balloon, a *ballooneau*, destined to receive and preserve the excess of gas produced by dilation, which will permit my balloon to undertake veritable long voyages, instead of remaining in the air two or three hours only, like our predecessors."

Nadar had sounded off too quickly. The Godard brothers, who were given the contract to build the *Giant*, had grave doubts about Verne's ingenious design. The engineers were blunt. No material existed to provide hermetic sealing of the hydrogen. The gas was bound to filter through the rubberized fabric and find its way to Verne's blowtorch in the cabin below. The blowtorch would heat the platinum head but it would also heat the hydrogen seeping through the bag and start a fire. The rapid circulation of the gas, as described by Verne, might be sufficient to ignite it spontaneously. Verne's invention might be good theory, but in practice it spelled inevitable disaster.

The anguished Nadar argued for a smaller bag beneath the larger envelope, instead of within it, to save some of the gas. The engineers pointed out that hydrogen would have to be released from the safety valve on top, simply to prevent the balloon from going up too high. A compensatory bag would simply add weight to a balloon, without serving any purpose. Reluctantly, Nadar had to abandon Verne's dream and his bitterness towards balloons returned. Privately, he spoke of his *Giant* as the last of her race. It was destined to become a mere money-maker to raise funds to build his helicopter, his "aeromotive."

When the *Giant* rose as high as the Notre Dame Cathedral, however, its imposing size made it the rage of Paris. The press marveled at the two-story wickerwork cottage suspended under the balloon. It would become the first "house" in history that would fly over the face of the earth. There were enough berths for fifteen passengers. The observation deck was piled high with grapnels, fowling pieces, speaking trumpets, carrier pigeons, and a wheel and an axle to carry the balloon when deflated. A collar of inflated India rubber would keep the cabin floating, if the balloon were forced down over water. Every preparation had been made for possible emergencies, including a Negro boy, who might prove useful in Africa. He called himself "Joe" after the Negro lad who was so heroic in *Five Weeks In A Balloon*. Impulsively, a Princess jumped aboard at the last moment. She had credentials to impress the Czar of Russia, and Nadar surmised that she might prove useful if the balloon reached Moscow.

The spectacular *Giant* rose to the firing of cannons, the salutes of the military, the "God Speed" of the Emperor and of the King of Greece, and a roar from a populace that had swept into the Champs de Mars without paying the franc admission. Poor Nadar had embarked on his voyage without paying off the costs.

One mile up, the wind became twice as strong and varied as much as thirty degrees in direction. The sun grew hot, and the balloon began to expand. The passengers were fascinated by the magic of villages that looked like children's toys, and rivers that were mere pencil lines. They could see boys jumping like mad, men firing guns at them, women making the sign of the cross. When the passengers glimpsed the white surf of the ocean approaching them, there were frantic cries to descend, immediately. The Zuyder Zee loomed ominously. Nadar valved a prodigious quantity of gas that vomited forth from the open valve on top with a tremendous noise. Fortunately, the balloon descended to a layer of wind that was blowing eastward, driving the ship away from the sea.

After a few hours of pleasant eating and toasting with champagne, and four hundred miles of travel, Nadar saw a white streak on the horizon. Actually, the changing weather was piling up a bank of clouds over Germany, but to Nadar it looked like the waves of the Atlantic shore. Had the balloon made a circle? Nadar pulled the rope with so frantic a desperation, he broke the valve line. Caught in a downdraft, the giant bag began plunging down at two yards a second. Bags of sand were thrown overboard too late. The air became a violent wind. "To the ropes! To the ropes!" The command sent every one clambering up the network of ropes.

The car struck the earth with a tremendous blow. The resilient wickerwork of the cabin prevented it from cracking. It bounced up again and down again. The crown of the safety valve was snapped back, holding in the remaining gas. There was no hope for the balloon to empty itself because the valve line had been torn off. The huge bag, still half full of gas, acted like an enormous sail, dragging the cumbersome car headlong, at thirty miles an hour, shredding trees.

The wind increased in violence, beating the huge bag to the ground like a drum head. Its anchor carried away the roof of a house. Helpless in the wind, the balloon kept making fifty-yard hops with blows that threatened to knock the car to pieces. Knees were bruised, ribs were broken, faces lacerated as the passengers tumbled about. Crazed with fear, some jumped overboard, only to lighten the weight of the car, making it rise higher.

Only then did Jules Godard, the fabricator of the balloon, realize his mistake in failing to add a rip panel, newly invented by the American, John Wise. It could have made a big enough hole to empty the *Giant* immediately. Feeling his responsibility, Godard risked his life to climb the network, holding a hatchet. In the shrieking gale, he chopped a hole in the silk large enough to empty the stinking coal gas. The huge bag fell like an exhausted monster to the ground. The passengers, painfully bruised, tumbled out and, led by Nadar, limped through the forest to the nearby town of Hanover.

Later, the *Giant* and the cabin were pulled into Hanover and shipped to Paris. After his bones had healed, the indomitable Nadar began the task of repairing his monster balloon. Although it ascended again in several cities of Europe, the gate receipts never recovered the costs. The dream of Verne had led Nadar to a fiasco.

But Verne's dream ship continued to haunt the aeronauts. A year later, the Godard brothers fabricated a new balloon, twice the size of the *Giant*. The populace was not awed; the great hulk was still at the mercy of the winds. People were asking why balloon-makers were not as bold and inventive as Verne's Dr. Fergusson? Though modest in size, Verne's *Victoria*, with its vertical control, had made a five weeks trip across Africa! Voices were raised in the press, demanding that engineers re-examine problems that once seemed too hard.

Even Nadar's dream came alive again in 1870 when a Prussian army surrounded Paris. This time, the government listened to his plea to build one hundred *Giants*. Verne had described his friend as a man "who had a love of the marvelous, carried to a total forgetfulness of self." Nadar imagined balloons 200 feet in diameter, capable of carrying sixty tons of explosives. The aerial army would sweep over the heads of the Prussians and shatter them in one massive assault. In desperation, the National Committee of Defense acted on his suggestion.

There was plenty of coal gas still available, but not enough silk to cover an armada of such huge balloons. Hundreds of seamstresses were put to work in two railroad stations to sew the numerous gores for the balloons, which were reduced to conventional size. It was soon discovered that there were only a handful of balloonists in Paris. Sailors were conscripted as pilots, supposedly because of their knowledge of winds and navigation. Within a matter of weeks, the first balloon was ready to fly out Gambetta, the Minister of the Interior, with a commission to raise an army in the provinces.

Balloons of 70,000 cubic feet capacity came off the assembly line, day after day, to be flown away at night over the surrounding German camps. The pilots had no previous experience. One landed, exhausted, in Norway. Five were lost in the North Sea. Nadar, himself, was able to return from Tours to Paris only after shooting down the one German balloon. On the whole, fifty-seven out of the sixty-six balloons made landed outside enemy lines, reaching the provinces, with sixty-seven passengers, carrier pigeons and three million letters.

Gambetta, once he escaped, organized a new French army that won a major battle at Orleans, defeating a Bavarian army corps. By the end of January, 1870, a new battle was shaping up at Le Mans, with 156,000 French troops poised to strike against 40,000 Germans, when the last of the Paris balloons brought the news that the Chamber of Deputies had voted to surrender. Nadar and his balloonists lost the chance of becoming the saviors of France. As it was, the ballooning

Balloon leaving Montmartre during the Siege of Paris.

enterprise, for France, was the only real success of the war.

The lesson was not lost on Germany. Paul Haenlein in 1872 created the first dirigible powered with an internal combustion engine. The Lenoir engine had a piston compressing coal gas within a revolving cylinder, setting off, stroke by stroke, 120 explosions a minute. The coal gas from the bag was piped into a car below, which held the engine. The dirigible managed to buck the wind and completed a round trip of twelve miles. But the primitive engine consumed as much as 250 cubic feet of gas an hour, dooming it for any long-distance flight.

Aeronauts then determined that if they could not make a long distance voyage, they would set, at least, a new altitude record. The challenge came from a doctor of medicine, Jean Bart, who made the startling claim that the state of stupor experienced in the upper atmosphere was not caused by mysterious gases, but by a simple lack of oxygen. He recommended that oxygen be compressed in bottles and sniffed through stopcock tubes by pilots when the atmosphere became too thin. An expedition was organized by Alexander Tissandier in 1875 to search out the truth of this claim.

When Tissandier and two distinguished scientists were four miles up, they decided to reserve the oxygen bottles for higher altitudes, so as to be sure to establish a new record. They thrilled to the radiance of light, the vastness and silence of space. Although they noted that their pulse rates had risen from 76 to 110 per minute, their brains registered no alarm. A subtle and insidious euphoria set in. They did not feel their hands becoming cakes of ice. Tissandier, alone, fumbled with the stopcock and succeeded in twisting it to sniff the escaping oxygen.

He revived instantly and suddenly became aware of the invidious enemy that had paralyzed his judgment. He turned to his companions in alarm, and discovered to his horror that their blue faces had already stiffened into rigor mortis. We know today that the state of rapture is a signal that only 30 seconds of consciousness remains.

The balloon had reached equilibrium at 26,000 feet. Tissandier pulled the valve rope and soon felt the breeze of descent on his face. Fully recovered, he made preparations for the dangerous down-run. He cut the grapnel rope just before crashing, and jettisoned enough weight to save himself from being hurled to the ground. The death of the two scientists raised such an outcry in the press, that the government forbade by law any further balloon flights to the top of the atmosphere.

Forbidden to make any altitude flights, Tissandier concentrated on creating an electric-powered dirigible. In 1883 he built a motor that developed 1.5 horsepower, but the weight of the batteries mounted up to 440 pounds, and another failure to create a long distance steerable balloon resulted. The following year, Charles Renard and D. C. Krebs tried out a new Gramme electric motor that produced more horsepower with the help of batteries weighing only 210 pounds. Their dirigible, *La France*, flew ten miles at twelve miles per hour under complete control, returning against the wind to the point of departure. But the batteries were exhausted. Once again, one could almost hear the mocking laughter of the vast mass of wind at man's puny efforts.

In the 1890's, a Norwegian, Andrée, seemed to have a scientific explanation of how he could steer a balloon across the North Pole from Norway to Alaska. He would use three 1,000 foot drag ropes, heavy enough to slow down the gas bag, so as to permit sails to catch the faster moving wind. He would angle the sails to the wind, in the same manner as a square-rigged ship, permitting him to steer against the wind as much as twenty-seven percent. Andrée's explanation was so plausible and convincing as to persuade the dynamite king, Alfred Nobel, to give him the funds to build such a balloon.

Andrée prepared himself for every contingency. His triple-decked wicker car carried a collapsible boat, a sled, food for three and a half months, guns and ammunition for a two year stay in the Arctic. He waited an entire year to get the exact wind he wanted. Finally, in 1897, a wind took him straight toward the North Pole at a speed of about twenty miles an hour. He expected to fly over the Pole in less than two days.

We know today what actually happened to Andrée and his two companions in the ill-fated *Eagle*. To begin with, they started out flying too low, 300 feet up. One of the drag lines tethered the balloon to a block of ice, trapping them for thirteen hours. After they discharged ballast, they were able to loosen the grapnel. Then the *Eagle* became airborne for sixty-five hours and thirty-three minutes—a world record. By that time, the fickle wind fooled them by dying down and constantly shifting directions. Gathering ice and hoar-frost, the *Eagle* was forced down about 500 miles from its starting point at eighty-three degrees north. Andrée and his two fellow Swedes decided to trek back to a depot, where they could live through the winter. They managed to reach White Island, where they built their winter home out of driftwood and whalebone.

Here they made their fatal mistake. They had built their makeshift tent under cliffs where the winds piled up snow during the night. The carbon monoxide gas from their Primus stove had no outlet. The men died in their sleep, unaware that their drowsiness was a painless prelude to death. The drifting snow actually buried them for thirty years before an unseasonable warm weather spell melted the snow to reveal their whereabouts to an observant fur trapper. Were it not for this unfortunate mischance, they could have easily survived the winter and returned to civilization, as

Nansen had the year before. Nothing, however, is a total loss. The mad adventure of Andrée was to turn the attention of a young Brazilian millionaire, Santos Dumont, from automobiles to balloons and to inspire a new wave of enthusiasm in French aeronautics.

The Years Without Horizons

In the world of heavier-than-air craft, meanwhile, a threat from Russia had accomplished what Cayley had failed to do—gather the aeronauts into a national society. A press release in 1866 announced that the Russian army was working on a "quintiplane," a huge flying machine with five sets of wings and ten flappers. A member of Parliament intoned, "The nation that conquers the air will rule the world." Jules Verne had just sent three aeronauts on a missile that crashed through the atmosphere after being blasted off to the moon. Verne's exhuberant story was written so convincingly that any technological achievement seemed possible. The aeronauts of England, alarmed by Russia and spurred by Verne, gathered and organized themselves into the Aeronautical Society of Great Britain. The goal was the creation of a heavier-than-air machine.

At the first meeting the members were surprised to learn how much original research had already been done by obscure investigators. The spirit of Cayley was abroad in England, after all, even though his name was never mentioned. Others were continuing the research he had suggested, but preferred to let themselves be known as original inventors.

In the papers read, all kinds of clues were being offered to the means by which the air might be conquered. F. H. Wenham's experiments proved for him that lift was derived mainly from the front portion of the cambered wing. Wings should be narrow and arranged one above the other to give greater support. He was the first to use the word aeroplanes.

The photographs of birds taken by J. B. Pettigrew revealed to him that the motions of the primary feathers (forward-downward and backward-upward) were equivalent to those of propeller blades. He suggested that propellers for models of aircraft change from simple flat windmills to curved blades tapering towards the tip and aft margins.

Birds, he continued, had an astonishing variety of almost imperceptible movements to preserve equilibrium. They balanced themselves in gusts of wind by giving each wing a different shape, constantly changing the stretch, curve and angle. And yet the wings worked in unison, reacting with each other. It should become clear, he concluded, that aeronauts had been following the wrong scent in simply duplicating the shape of a bird's wings and flapping them.

It was decided that aeronauts would display all their latest models in an aeronautic room at the Crystal Palace exhibition of 1868. An astonishing variety of models were shown. Wenham followed his own suggestion. His aeroplane had six narrow planes one above the other. In a test, he himself, lay prone on a carrier beneath the lowest wing. A wind lifted his aeroplane only to smash it to the ground again. Apparently he had not understood Cayley's principles of control.

Matthew Boulton had small, hinged, winged surfaces at the tips of wings that could be swivelled up and down—displaying a method to parallel the actions of the feathers of a bird. He had a patent pending on an airplane. Gabriel de la Landelle's steam model of a helicopter had two superimposed rotors and an aluminum boiler, but its lifting power was only equal to two-thirds of its weight. The stumbling block, as usual, was the lack of light and powerful engines.

John Stringfellow had taken, finally, Cayley's advice and built a triplane. Three wings, stretching ten feet, were arranged one above the other to give greater support. Its *nacelle* (body) rested on a three wheel undercarriage and it had twin propellers driven by a one cylinder steam engine, generating

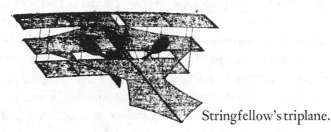

Stringfellow's triplane.

one-third of a horsepower. This small steam engine proved to be the sensation of the exhibition. It weighed less than twelve pounds and its ratio made it the most remarkable power plant of its time. Everyone buzzed with anticipation before the test of the model in the Palace gardens. The model was suspended on a wire. The engine was started. The propellers sent the craft forward, but when it left the wire for a free flight it could not sustain itself. Stringfellow had not taken the pains to study Cayley's aerodynamics of lift. A hop was not a flight. However, he won a consolation prize of 100 pounds for his engine.

Another lesser brain than Cayley, Thomas Moy of the Aeronautic Society, later claimed he had the answer to flight. He said that a heavier-than-air machine needed to attain a speed of 150 miles an hour before it would gather the lifting pressure it needed for flight. He built an aerial model with two huge dual propellers, to be turned by a three-horsepower steam engine. The whole device weighed 120 pounds. When tethered to a circular track set up at the Crystal Palace gardens, Moy's plane rose only six inches, even though the six-foot propellers swept 550 revolutions per minute. There was so little known about aerodynamics, that one reporter claimed that Moy's machine had hopeful features because it had a small proportion of fixed surface and a great amount of movable surface! With the confidence of ignorance, Moy claimed it would have succeeded if the machine were made life size.

In France, the enigma of flight was being tackled by a young genius, Alphonse Penaud (1850-1880). Like Cayley, he began his career with a flying toy. Heavier-than-air flight, in fact, had its only triumphs among the world of children. Three kinds of automatic toys on the market were steady best sellers, and kept alive the dreams of flight in the minds of the young. Those with flapping wings were called ornithopters, those with propellers on top that rose straight up were named helicopters, and the fixed wing type became known as gliders. Children had the thrill of watching for a few seconds their mechanical toys zooming through the air.

At the age of twenty-one, Alphonse Penaud was smitten with the urge to improve the flying toy. He built a mechanical model of a glider that he called a *Planophore*. It was a twenty-inch stick with eighteen-inch wings, shaped like a bird. He added a tail unit aft of the wings, and for added equilibrium, the wings about half-way down the stick were given a dihedral angle. After experimenting, he discovered that the tail plane was most efficient if set downward at an angle of eight degrees.

For power, Penaud introduced twisted rubber to turn an eight-inch pusher propeller of feathers. He was careful to place the center of gravity just behind the leading edge of the wings at the point of greatest air pressure. And he had learned enough about aerodynamics to bend the outer edges of the wings to give it the final touch of lateral stability. One could have sworn that he had copied Cayley, but historians say he

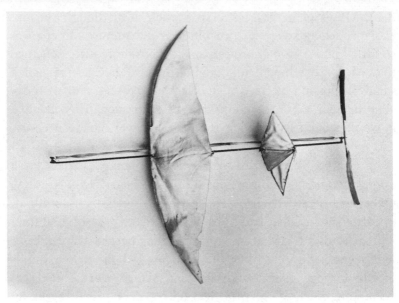

Model of Penaud Planophore. *Smithsonian Institution.*

became aware of Cayley only years later, in 1876, when the Aeronautical Society of England published, at last, an abridged version of Cayley's 1810 article.

Penaud demonstrated his new model to the *Société de Navigation Aerienne* in the Tuilleries Gardens. The group of aerial enthusiasts, called on to witness an important demonstration, were peeved at first when they learned that they were to witness the test of an invention by a mere youth. But they saw the *Planophore* fly 131 feet in eleven seconds, a world record for a flying toy. They agreed that the young man had proven without a doubt that a heavier-than-air machine could fly, and they expected great things from the young genius.

Inspired by this encouragement, Penaud and his friend, the mechanic Gauchet, worked an entire year together and patented a design for a fixed-wing biplane. Every possible aspect had been carefully considered by the precocious students. The wings were dihedral and cambered. They added a hinged moving section on the edge of the wing, which they called an aileron. The elevator and rudder in the rear were a vertical fin unit that could be controlled by the pilot with a single stick. The pilot would find it simple to move the "joy stick" right and left to control the rudder and fore and aft to move the elevator up and down.

The design gave the airplane two propellers with four blades each. The boat-like fuselage was capable of landing the plane on water. A fully retractable tricycle gear gave it an easy landing on the ground. A glass cockpit dome was designed to shield the pilot's head from the wind.

All the necessary adaptive mechanisms had been added. There was the vertical fin to assist in controlling the direction of flight. It had a crosspiece on the tail to prevent the nose of the aircraft from pitching. The ailerons dropped easily to stabilize the plane in gusts of wind. Flaps on front could be raised to slow up the plane on descending. The rudder was made large enough to permit the plane to swing around. The young man of twenty-six had achieved the miracle plane of the century in 1876.

Even while Penaud was trying to raise the money to build the plane, he was struggling to invent for it a new kind of internal combustion engine that would be light in weight and still have the output of thirty horsepower needed to propel the plane at sixty miles an hour.

He was a sickly young man with a bone disease, which was progressively becoming worse. Doctors did not give him too many years to live. That was bad enough, but what really broke his heart was the lack of vision among the engineers, who dismissed his design as a chimera. Who would dare risk his neck on such untried innovations? Penaud would gladly have done so, but he was unable to win any financial support. The money that should have gone to him went instead to the experiments of Moy and Du Temple, both of whom succeeded only in hopping their planes. The French War Ministry provided money to a Russian engineer, A. N. Lodygin, to build an electrically operated helicopter. No one believed that anyone as young as Penaud was could have achieved the impossible.

Penaud knew he had invented an airplane capable of flying. He pleaded to deaf ears for the money to build his plane. The silence in reply was too much for him. His illness became progressively worse. And now there was the haunting knowledge that Cayley had known how to build an airplane seventy years before. Cayley had understood the need for initial velocity, for lightness and strength, for the cambered dihedral wing, for the biplane construction with struts and diagonal bracing. Penaud knew his measurements on the angle of the wings in flight and the pressures on the wings concurred with Cayley's. No one had understood the signals that Cayley had given. Why should anyone listen to a young man, not yet thirty, who gave the same signals? At the age of thirty Penaud committed suicide. On his deathbed he ordered all of his designs to be buried with him.

New designs followed each other, year after year. There was a huge, single blade screw propeller with a spread of 178 feet. The blades were made hollow and light. A fan drove a stream of air through the hollow blades, and the air escaped from their tips. The inventor hoped the blast of air would cause the blades to revolve by jet reaction.

This suggested to Enrico Forlanni that he might lift a helicopter by making it free of the weight of fuel and fire. He slung a copper sphere under the helicopter. It rested on the ground and was filled with water over a fire, which developed sufficient steam to power a light steam engine in the helicopter. The high pressure steam raced up through a pipe to activate the engine and the rotor. When the pipe was disconnected, the helicopter, free of the weight of any fuel or fire, rose to a height of forty-two feet. For the first time, the helicopter dream was made real, but only for twenty seconds. It dramatized the need, more sharply than ever, for a light-weight engine.

Since no such practical engine existed, Horatio Phillips in 1884 tackled the problem from another angle. He theorized that he could double the lifting power of the propeller blades by reshaping them. Scientists claimed that most of the pressure was on the narrow, front edge of the blades. Phillips made them as narrow as Venetian blinds. He used fifty such blades, tapering and curving at each end and tethered to a weird contraption chained to a circular track. Whirling at forty miles an hour, his blades lifted his model to a height of 250 feet. The weight-power ratio was raised dramatically with one horsepower of steam sustaining seventy-two pounds in the air. Phillips laid the foundation of aerofoil design for blades, but the practical helicopter was still beyond the grasp of the brave inventors.

But still by 1885 no heavier-than-air machine had really been lifted and maintained in the air; no suitable engine was available. Every hope had been dashed and the word *impossible* was being freely used. "No possible combination of known substances, known forms of machinery and known forms of forces could be united in a practical machine by which man shall fly long distances through the sky."

The future never looked blacker for a practical air transport. The feeling of hopelessness had become universal. It looked very much as if the laws of nature were in a conspiracy to prevent the flight of man.

There were plenty of reasons for this mood of pessimism. The director of the U.S. Patent Office had resigned, because, as he explained, all the basic patents had already been issued. The universe with all its evolution and energies had been most thoroughly mapped. University graduates were told there was nothing left for them to do except to fill in some details. The French Academy of Science would accept no more papers on perpetual motion, the squaring of the circle, directional control of balloons, and heavier-than-air machines, lumping all these projects as a waste of time. The laws of science as well as of Nature made the conquest of the air a hopeless quest.

The Ship of the Sky

WHEN OTHERS HAD GIVEN UP, JULES VERNE EMBARKED UPON writing a fantasy of a heavier-than-air machine; he had become convinced that man was nearer to the conquest of the air than was generally realized. He felt a compelling duty to stand up against the wave of futility. He was the most popular writer of his time and felt he should use his influence to bring courage to the timid and faint of heart.

He wrote hopefully, "I can imagine a helicopter made out of a new kind of material, harder than steel, lighter than aluminum. It could go straight up or down, fly sideways, hover at one point and then instantly speed away like a meteor."

Verne knew, however, that such a miracle in the air could never be made real, unless he first solved the problem of the light and powerful engine. Edison had stated in 1880, such an engine would have to weigh only three pounds per horsepower. In his quest to lift a helicopter, Edison had tested a lightweight engine fueled with stock ticker tape spaced with bits of explosives and ignited by electric sparks. He almost lost his life experimenting with this and turned his genius to other inventions.

Drawing of plane proposed by Edison in 1880.

Verne continued where Edison left off. However, like
Edison, he decided on a helicopter rather than an airplane for
his heavier-than-air machine—for reasons of safety alone. The
very idea of flying an airplane brought a feeling of anxiety.
Where was the guarantee there would always be sufficient
airflow? Suppose the motor failed or a plane was too slow on
making a turn? Without minimal airflow, lift would vanish.
The plane would dive and drop like a rock.

The man in a helicopter, in contrast, would have a feeling
of security. It could always manage a safe, parachute-like
descent. It had no need of a preliminary run, an inclined runway or a launching catapult. The helicopter promised to be
able to rise and land from any place a man could live and
this offered the possibility of door-to-door transportation.

During a trip to the Mediterranean in 1884 Jules Verne
spent some hours in a private room of a Milan library. He
was shown the original notebooks of Leonardo Da Vinci that
had not yet been published or translated and which were
unknown at that time. Da Vinci's design of a helicopter with
its helical rotor supported by a universal joint left an indelible
imprint upon his mind.

But where was the energy to lift a helicopter? Verne, who
devoured everything in print pertaining to science, had
studied the potential of an internal combustion engine.

De Rochas had published the principle of the four-stroke
cycle in 1862, and Otto had built such an engine in 1876. It
was a ponderous machine, turning over at little more than

200 revolutions per minute with two series of explosions that would shake a helicopter to pieces. Verne, unfortunately, did not know that Gottlieb Daimler had tested a new engine that year of 1885 that used the new derivative of petroleum, gasoline. This made it possible to speed up explosions to 800 per minute and reduce the weight to eighty-eight pounds. Cayley's dream had been fulfilled, at last.

Even if Verne had read about it, he would not have seen the importance of that event. He missed completely the use of chemical fuels in the evolution of energy. Manpower, horsepower, rail, steam and electricity were the requisites of power for mankind. It would have surprised him to learn what a role hydrocarbons were destined to play in the rise of civilization.

Instead, his mind turned to the potential of electricity, leaping to the equivalent of the electric fuel cell of today. The existing battery power was disappointing. Krebs had flown his dirigible the year before with an array of batteries that produced only nine horsepower. The batteries had been exhausted after only twelve miles of air travel.

Nevertheless, Verne asked himself if there might not be an electric battery in the future with far more potential. His imagination condensed all the power of Edison's giant dynamos that were illuminating New York into small "accumulators." Like the genie of the *Arabian Nights*, this power could be confined within a bottle one moment and, when uncorked, could mushroom powerfully across the sky.

Verne's miraculous unit with its six-month supply of electrical power has begun to cross the frontier of reality in the Gemini 5 fuel cell that constantly recirculates oxygen and hydrogen from water to gas to ions, and back to water, to start the cycle again. On our horizon there is looming the "pinch plasma" engine that turns water into a fourth state of matter—electronically charged particles pinched by a magnetic field and shot out of the compression chamber at tremendous velocities. Energy, "up to infinity," out of water, may be available sooner than we realize.

Having convinced himself that "energy up to infinity" was a scientific possibility, Verne's imagination conceived of a helicopter, enlarged to the size of an ocean vessel. If a mouse could be lifted into the air, so could an elephant. Had not Bishop Wilkins written in 1691, "A giant ship swims as well as a small cork, and an eagle flies as well as a gnat?" It led Verne to imagine his helicopter with a forest of masted propellers, making of it a veritable "clipper ship" of the sky. For Verne the conquest of the air was entering a new stage.

Verne enjoyed creating a mechanism just as he enjoyed creating ingenious plots for his stories. He set out to be the master assembler of the scattered components left behind by many designers of aircraft. He wanted the machine for his story, *Clipper Ship of the Clouds* to be as valid as any paper read before a scientific society; so he chose those elements that conformed to basic aerodynamics, making a new unity of them.

He understood, for example, the many conflicting problems that a helicopter would have to overcome. The blades of the rotor in advancing moved faster and developed more lift than they did on retreating, creating a mishmash of forces. So Verne gave his rotors so fast a spinning force that the speed of the helicopter was very much slower in comparison, canceling out the contrary variations in the velocities of blades that attacked the wind. He was unaware of the fact that a rotor can take only so much rotation before it tears itself to pieces.

To achieve a smooth flow of gliding forces, Verne gave his plastic ship thirty-seven rotors, each responsible for a pair of contra-rotating propellers. Two enormous four-bladed propellers at the prow and the stern gave the vehicle forward speed, a principle being used in the rotary aircraft built today.

He planned his design with detailed, technical care. Three constructions rose above the deck of the ninety-foot sky ship. One held the machinery for the electrical accumulator; the second contained the kitchen with its electric stove; the third comprised the group of cabins. One of the cabins was roofed with a dome of glass for the helmsman. And since Verne was an omnivorous reader, he had to find space for a library in one of the cabins. He also managed to squeeze into the same space both a portable printing press and an India rubber boat. Below the bridge deck were the storerooms for water, ammunition and the raw materials for the accumulator that would have to be replenished every six months. Most important of all to Verne, his ship was capable of 125 miles per hour speed. "The speed is that of the storm which tears up trees by the roots." In short, his rotary winged aircraft, by using the whole force of her propellers, could fly around the world in 200 hours, or less than eight days. In 1885, this was almost inconceivable.

Verne named this clipper ship of the clouds, the *Albatross*, honoring Captain Le Bris. Like the fabulous bird of the sea, Verne's mechanical marvel was perfectly adapted to its element and brought all the comforts of home to its eight passengers.

Verne used his *Clipper Ship of the Clouds* to preach a sermon on the future. He was deeply concerned with the military advances of science. He feared they might make it easier for unscrupulous dictators to hypnotize mobs into wars of aggression for world conquest. Thus, he had the hero of his story, Robur, plan to use his mechanical marvel to unite the nations of the world into a Utopia of peace, brotherhood, and democracy. Verne imagined that his fantastic vehicle would arouse the people of the world to a mass enthusiasm for the new science that could reshape society according to the laws of reason and mathematics. With scientists in control, it would be possible, at last, to plan for the future. Verne stated that his *Albatross* was a symbol to represent the future of science.

The enemies of Robur were the reactionary balloonists. He kidnapped these stick-in-the-mud conservatives to show them the wonders of his heavier-than-air machine. He tried to persuade them to join him in an open conspiracy to unite the nations of the world against the menace of militarism.

The balloonists in *Clipper Ship of the Clouds* were lovers of tradition and believed Robur to be a dangerous madman. They spurned his international dream and managed to escape. Back on their home grounds, they arranged to demonstrate before the populace the efficiency of their new dirigible, *Go Ahead*, hoping to attain an altitude record. Suddenly, a new and swifter *Albatross* arrived on the scene. Believing they were being attacked, the balloonists rose up to 16,000 feet, disappearing from view of the earth. The hydrogen bag expanded and exploded. Robur, with his swift *Albatross*, circled below the plummeting basket and maneuvered skillfully to its side, where the passengers jumped to the safety of the mechanized ship.

Having proven the superiority of his heavier-than-air machine, Robur lectured the stunned crowd in bitter tones. New inventions, he said, demanded great social changes. People must reorganize their lives to a machine age that must constantly change and expand. Without this vision a nation was doomed to remain backward.

Published in 1886, Verne's story became so great a success, that the Smithsonian Institution in Washington, D.C. included Verne's phantom ship of the air in its pictorial display of the history of flight. His clipper ship, with its cloud of rotors instead of sails, stands out like an exotic print amid all the familiar designs. The comment beneath the picture is sober and to the point. The ship had the capacity to hover at 8,700 feet and fly with the speed of 125 miles per hour.

Fifty years later, the Sikorsky helicopter was to have almost similar capabilities, even to the eight-man crew.

We know today that over the centuries, Archimedes, da Vinci and Sikorsky were the giant stepping stones from the concept to the reality of the helicopter. Archimedes foreshadowed the helicopter with his screw. Leonardo Da Vinci conceived of a vehicle. Igor I. Sikorsky made it work. Inspired in his youth by Verne's imaginary ship of the sky, Sikorsky grew up to make that dream a reality in 1939.

Unfortunately, the impact of the *Albatross* in Verne's generation led to a misdirected effort. *Clipper Ship of the Clouds* intoxicated aeronauts with its fantasy of great power. It led engineers in the final years of the nineteenth century to become less concerned with the aerodynamics of wing shapes and air currents than with mechanisms of brute force. As much as a million dollars was spent in attempts to get a machine airborne by sheer power, as if a heavier-than-air machine need only be pushed through the air as was a train or a ship on the ground. It was as if the nineteenth century mind, outside of Cayley and Penaud, could not grasp the nature of the media they had to use for support. All efforts ended in failure.

The Flying Automatons

WHILE SCIENCE FICTION IMAGINED THE WONDER ENGINE OF THE future, and engineers struggled to make the clumsy internal combustion engine practical, one professor, Samuel P. Langley, who taught physics at the University of Pittsburgh, began to re-examine the heavier-than-air machine from a new angle. He wondered about the physical forces that allowed Penaud's flying toy to maintain its equilibrium during a flight of 200 feet. He sensed that the toy was no mere trifle, but a flying automaton that might be made big enough to hold a man. He marveled that while academies continued to forecast with gloomy finality the impossibility of heavier-than-air flight, excited boys wound up the rubber-band motors of their mechanical birds and hurled them into the air.

Langley realized that Penaud had made his flying toy inherently stable, that the precise position of the wings in relation to the tail unit was a balancing arrangement that revealed a hidden law of nature. He faced the same questions that had intrigued Cayley and Penaud. These men were unknown to him, and to solve the mystery they had solved, he had to retrace the steps that they had already taken.

With the same concern for precision, Langley decided to make careful measurements. He built a giant whirling table with wooden arms that extended thirty feet. They swept through a circumference of 200 feet at all speeds up to seventy miles per hour. At the end of each arm, he suspended a spring balance and wing shapes of every variety and weight. To his astonishment, he discovered that a suspended object, weighing one pound, when whirled at seventy miles an hour, was reduced in weight to less than one ounce.

The implications were as tremendous to him as they had been to Cayley. Here was no mere conjecture, made by Nadar in a previous generation, that an ice skater could save himself from breaking through thin ice if his speed were swift enough. This whirling table also measured the "internal work of the wind" and revealed eventually that if a one horsepower motor drove a small surface at express-train speed, it would be able to support 200 pounds of weight. There was in moving air a power of a greater magnitude than was commonly supposed. Langley wrote a scientific paper with the conclusion, "so far as the mere power to sustain heavy bodies in the air by mechanical flight goes, such mechanical flight is possible with engines we now possess."

It was the first time in anyone's memory that an esteemed scientist had spoken with authority on a subject that had been generally regarded as a refuge of cranks. His papers on flight created such a sensation, they persuaded the majority of engineers that the twenty-century-old problem of aviation might be solved after all. The climate of opinion changed overnight. Even Cayley's paper was resurrected and repub-lished in scientific journals.

A new argument was heard among aeronauts. Flight might be impossible for dirigibles or helicopters, but not for air-planes. Once an airplane was catapulted or speeded sufficiently down a long runway, steam engines then available could give it the necessary lift to let it soar through the air. All that was required was the money to build such a heavier-than-air machine.

Henson's 1840 dream of a giant plane was taken up again. This time, two wealthy men pledged their fortunes to the building of such a machine: Clement Ader, who had made a fortune installing the Bell Telephone in France, and Hiram Maxim, whose rapid-fire machine gun assured him an enormous income.

Ader had already experimented and failed with a flapping contrivance; Maxim had failed to lift a helicopter he had worked on. But Ader had been in Arabia, installing telephones, and had been impressed by the vultures that soared without flapping. He conjectured that a fixed-wing plane might do likewise if it were built to work in accordance with the same laws of power, weight and speed. It was Penaud's idea, this time come alive in a man who had the health, money and engines that Penaud had lacked.

The result was the *Éole*, remarkable in that it had elements we see in airplanes today. Ader's *Éole* was an unbraced monoplane with tapered wings, wheeled undercarriage, closed cockpit and foldable wings that could be swept back. It had the lightest of steam engines available, which, with a weight-power ratio of 3 to 1, according to nine witnesses, just managed to lift the plane and its equipment into the air for a hop of 160 feet.

The amount of power that could be obtained from every unit weight of power plant had become one of the central factors in powered flight. The Ader steam engine, with a 3 to 1 ratio, was barely sufficient to lift the machine off the ground. Today, however, official France credits him with the first powered flight.

In his patent specifications, Ader claimed that he used a vertical rudder to control direction of flight. He controlled pitch by the contractibility of his wing surface so as to maintain a balance between the "centers of pressure of the air on the surfaces and the center of gravity of the aircraft." He stated that lateral stability could be maintained by warping the wing tips.

Ader used the bat wing as his wing prototype because it was aerodynamically better for slow speeds than the lesser cambered bird's wings. His propellers were flexible, moving at different speeds, so as to give them variable pitch. His *Avion Number 2*, his third plane, had two engines so that the contra-rotating propellers could be varied by varying the engine power. But even with all of this, he did not comprehend control. His study of vultures had convinced him that birds attained lateral stability simply by deepening the camber of the wings. Thus Ader simply arranged to bend down the tips of the wings. This, as later experiments proved, was not enough.

In 1897 a flight Ader had great hopes for was a fiasco. There was a heavy wind and his plane was overturned and smashed. The military, which had been helping him, lost interest in advancing further experimentation. He was almost

Ader's own sketch of his 1890 Éole.

bankrupt. Without the backing of government funds, he could not persist. Something snapped in Ader and he lost all interest in going on. He lived to see the triumph of the airplane, but his name was all but forgotten.

Hiram Maxim started his search for a soaring machine before the gasoline motor became really practical. Since he had to use the bulky, heavy steam engine, he realized he would have to build a mammoth of the air. He invested $150,000 in elaborate preparations. Guided by Langley's papers, he built a wind tunnel and 200-foot whirling arms to study wing lift, balance, and the thrust of propellers. But he became impatient with the professional mathematicians, who believed all problems could be solved by formulas. He felt he could rely on brute power alone.

Maxim had as great an imagination as Jules Verne. So he began to build a metal monster with an enormous 110-foot monoplane wing and five hinged planes on either side to provide control for equilibrium—5,500 square feet of surface in all. The body of the plane was 145 feet long, tip to tail, and the twin propellers were immense paddles of seventeen feet, six inches each. This tremendous creation, with a weight of 3.5 tons plus the weight of three passengers, was to be lifted by steam engines, heated by burning benzine, and was to generate 360 horsepower. The steel tubing of the framework was also used as a circulation system by which used steam was condensed to water to be used over again. As a matter of fact, he created such a powerful airplane engine, it was not surpassed until twenty-five years later when the Liberty engine of World War I proved capable of generating 400 horsepower.

Maxim speculated that a forty mile-per-hour speed would be enough to lift his leviathan. To get the necessary speed, he mounted his giant on a wheeled undercarriage that could grip railway tracks, stretching eighteen hundred feet. His first goal was simply to lift his air monster, and he added a safety outrigger that ran on the underside of dual guard rails to keep it from soaring. The machine would be able to lift itself only six inches.

On July 31, 1894, after many years of work, the air giant was ready for the final test. After building up a high steam pressure of 200 pounds, Sir Hiram and an assistant climbed aboard. Maxim pulled the throttle. The machine started moving over the railroad track, quickly gathering speed up to forty miles an hour as it raced along the track. Within five seconds, he felt the plane lift and tug beneath the under-pass, eager to be airborne.

Suddenly, the unexpected happened. He heard the grinding, tearing sound of the underpass wheel breaking the heavy squared pine logs of the guard rail. Another moment, and he would be in the air, flying. Once in the air, would he be able to control the plane's equilibrium? The heavy plane might plunge to the ground. Panicked, Maxim thrust his throttle forward, shutting off the power. But its momentum kept the plane on its shrieking, tearing path, plowing through a crash barrier at the end of the run.

Maxim emerged intact. He had saved his life by quick thinking. Strangely enough, he felt elated. He had succeeded in creating a lift greater than the three ton weight of the aircraft and the crew—the goal he had sought. He even boasted that propulsion and lift were now solved problems, although the truth was that they were not. But he also knew now that air could not be conquered by brute force alone. He still faced the formidable problem of control after the plane was airborne. This would mean years of experimenting and costs, that might become a bottomless pit. His struggle simply to lift a plane had exhausted him. He had no heart to go on, and he turned his inventive genius to other spheres.

The word *impossible* was used again by the authorities.

Professor Simon Newcomb cited the square-cube law as a grim barrier to heavier-than-air flight. If you increase any surface four times the weight will become eight times greater. Therefore, if you increase a mechanical bird to life size, the weight problem becomes an insurmountable barrier. And he was right, with the engines then available.

A state commission in Berlin, under the chairmanship of the world-famous scientist, Ludwig von Helmholtz, applied the square-cube law to muscle-powered flight and issued their scientific verdict that it would be impossible. Many misunderstood the verdict and believed any kind of heavier-than-air flying was hopeless. At M.I.T. the verdict was "hopeless" and the great scientist Kelvin said, "I have not the smallest molecule of faith in aerial navigation other than ballooning."

However, Langley, who had become the head of the Smithsonian Institution, still proclaimed blithely the coming advent of the airplane. He argued that a mechanical bird could be made foolproof, automatically stable. A correct, built-in mechanism, based on laws of aerodynamics, would not require the human intelligence of a pilot to balance itself in the air. The pilot need only steer it. Langley maintained that a pilot could fly even a motorless glider around the world if it did not meet with exceptional moments of calm.

To vindicate this theory, he decided to build a flying automaton. He relied on laboratory experiments in wind tunnels and turning tables to provide the mathematical figures of weight, stress, lift, drag, shape and speed of different wing forms. He made and tested more than 100 rubber-tensioned models. And from there went on to build larger models, about fourteen feet in span, which he termed "aerodromes" from the Greek word meaning "air runners."

His final choice was a tandem monoplane, with two pairs of wings placed one behind the other, fastened to the body at a small dihedral angle. It had a pivoted tail controlled by springs. The thirteen-foot model of steel was powered by a steam engine of one horsepower that weighed only seven pounds.

On May 6, 1896, in the presence of Alexander Graham Bell and several other friends, Langley catapulted this flying machine model into the air from a houseboat on the Potomac River. It rose 100 feet into the air and flew at thirty miles per hour. Three-quarters of a mile away, the propeller stopped. At this point, the Aerodrome did not plunge like a stone to the ground. It came down slowly and gracefully as a bird and settled on the Potomac without any damage. Langley's assistant, the skilled mechanic, Charles Manly, exulted: "For the first time in the history of the world, a device produced by a man has actually flown through the air, and has preserved its equilibrium without the aid of a guiding human intelligence." It seemed at that moment that man was on the verge of successful mechanical flight.

The Gleam of Science Fiction

H.G. WELLS BEGAN THINKING OF THE FUTURE WORLD OF
flight in the days when Ader, Maxim and Langley were
familiar names in the dream of air conquest. It was still the
Victorian Age—a world of little isolated houses built of
bricks, blackened with soot from smoky chimneys. The
wealthy were sporting with chugging quadricycles; the roads
were dusty, sloppy after rain, and pitted by wagon wheels.
Very few anticipated that the automobile would become
the pacemaker in the near future. Instead, the prevailing feeling was that the highway of the air would soon become
wide open for unheard of speeds and widespread transport.

Wells began his imaginative journey into the future of
flight with a short story in 1895, about the ordeal of a mechanical inventor struggling to create a flying machine. The
pioneer astronaut hero studies the flight of rooks and gulls,
which cover enormous distances with scarcely a perceptible
movement of their wings. He builds his plane on the basis
of his observations. Among other things, it has a pin that
permits each wing to be tilted at a small angle, independent
of its fellow. "The instantaneous adjustments of the wings,

the quick response to a passing breeze, the giddy, eddying movement that require such absolute precision—all that he must learn, learn with infinite labor and infinite danger, if ever he is to conquer flying."

The plane is launched with the method used by Maxim. As the plane soars, so does the spirit of the aeronaut, dazzled by the stunning landscape as seen for the first time from the air. Now comes the critical point—the dangerous curve in making a turn. The pilot, with no experience, turns the spoked wheel too far, causing the plane to plunge steeply downward. The hills, so lovely before, are now a deadly menace rushing up to meet him. The flying machine is out of control, its momentum plunging it to its smashing doom on the ground.

Wells concludes that many necks would have to be broken before man learned to fly. In lives and in treasure, the cost of the conquest of the air would be more enormous than had been spent on man's great conquest of the sea. The weight of the plane spelled both doom and hope. Only a machine heavier than air could go through the air against the wind, and man must resolve to control it, despite all the dangers.

By 1897, in his novel *When the Sleeper Awakes,* Wells can imagine superhighways, automobiles and television, but his imagination falters with future flight. His concept of the air transport of the future tells us more of the time when he wrote his novel than of the future he purported to predict. The plane he presented was a flimsy, fragile giant. Its wings, spread out to 600 feet and more, were made of some sort of glossy, artificial membrane, braced with metal wires, almost like the nerves of a bee's wing. The seats for the passengers were slung below, swing fashion, to absorb the vibrations which movement through a moderate wind was supposed to produce. The passengers were to have only a bit of canvas to protect them from the brunt of the wind. Wells claimed that this strange vehicle could race around the earth at 90 miles an hour, carrying 200 tons of weight.

Wells had no confidence that an engine could be made sufficiently powerful to sweep a plane into the air by racing on the ground. He felt that a special sort of swift car was needed to thrust it into the air. The car and plane had to be raised by elevators to the top of a huge girded construction resembling the roller coaster of an amusement park, which he calls the "flying stage." The car supports the plane and races down a mile-long inclined track with ever increasing speed, until the plane can take off into the air on its own power.

Wells struggled valiantly to comprehend how his gigantic air machine could remain stable in the air. He follows the clues of Wenham and Penaud to permit otherwise rigid wings to change their shape with hinged borders, but adds cumbersome details.

Wells also predicted small private planes. He wrote about insect-like private fliers, which he named "aeropiles." They could be converted to automobiles simply by adding pneumatic wheels. But to be launched into the air, they still required a special sort of swift car to give them the initial momentum to become airborne. To land his plane, Wells shut off the power, converting the plane into a motorless glider.

Wells foresaw an age of huge airports, of squadrons of machines flying in close formation like a flock of migrant birds or lined up outside hangars like a herd of cows in a pasture. But he was best at describing the psychological reaction to the new experience of flying. He sensed it would not be easy for earth-bound man to take to the air. Passengers would have to drink a mixture containing ergot to prevent air sickness, besides overcoming the psychological fear of moving unsupported through the air.

Despite the discomforts, Wells expected travelers to be exhilarated by the sense of swift flight. Drawing deep breaths of the sweet, pure air, the passengers would experience a sort of intoxication. As the machine swooped down a spiral, dove like a hawk, and swept up like a skylark, the sensation would intensify to the point where the desire to shout became irresistible.

The end of the century was a psychological moment for man to look forward to a new age and a new world. The eyes of man turned upward to the atmosphere and to space. The reading public had been familiar with machines that could hurl a man around the earth, or to the moon for that matter, ever since Edward Everett Hale and Jules Verne had begun describing them. New stories such as the serial the *New York Journal* was running under the headline, *Edison Conquers Mars*, surprised no one. Hideous Martians invaded the earth. A crash program in Edison's invention factory came forth in record time with a perfected flying machine and an electric ray gun that disintegrated the alien species in one white flash. For younger readers there was the paperback novel of April, 1898, *The Sinking Star, or Frank Reade, Jr.'s Trip Into Space with His New Airship, Saturn.*

In Germany Kurt Lasswitz was describing in plausible scientific detail the three rocket engine that would be necessary to achieve a successful orbital flight. In Russia, Tsiolkovski was applying mathematics to the exhaust velocity of burning kerosene and oxygen. He discovered to his joy that it was greater than the explosive bursts of dynamite or TNT. It led him to dream of future castles in space, in which man could live blissfully with less strain on his heart than on the terrestrial globe.

Man felt the delightful shiver of contemplating these far-out dreams of space flight—fairy tales that might actually turn out to be true.

When Jules Verne began to re-appraise the possibility of flight, he proved to be a better engineer than H. G. Wells. By this time Verne realized that his dream of atomic energy, which had propelled his *Albatross* fifteen years before, had become actual fact with the Curie experiments. But the practical application of this energy belonged to the far future.

The internal combustion engine, by contrast, was making sensational progress, "threatening the locomotive steam engine." Verne's imagination switched from electric to compressed gas motors. Verne imagined an internal combustion engine of compressed air that was light yet powerful enough to propel an airplane. He prided himself on having an artist's disciplined imagination.

In his *City of the Sahara* Verne was the first to conceive a combination of a helicopter and an airplane. His imaginary V-STOL was more practical than the multirotored helicopter he had described years before in his *Clipper Ship of the Clouds*.

Verne knew that every gas can be liquefied, so long as it is sufficiently compressed and the temperature is low enough. He placed his liquefied gas in the same kind of thermos container we use today to hold the liquefied oxygen and hydrocarbons in our rocket engines. The liquid need only flow out to atmospheric pressure to regain its gaseous state. Verne regulated this flow by a process of valves and tubes to feed an inner chamber, which was always kept warm. He must have read about Daimler's first engine, where the vaporized fuel was ignited and exploded in a chamber by a permanent gas flame.

But Verne went beyond Daimler to dream up a gas turbine, applying it to aircraft a generation before the inventor of the jet engine, Frank Whittle. When the liquid air returned to its gaseous state, it exerted sufficient pressure to whirl the turbine blades that powered the helicopter rotor on top. This lifted the machine off the ground. The lift was made easier by the fact that the wings of his plane, like those of a bird, were furled and rested against the fuselage. Once his machine was raised into the air, the wings swung open and the propeller blades shifted from vertical to horizontal.

As he went on to describe the airpline of the twentieth century, Verne revealed a surprising grasp of aerodynamics. He understood the difficulties of pitch, roll and yaw, of keeping an airplane buffeted by air currents in perfect balance.

Verne devoted special attention to a mechanical stabilizer. "When a bird meets the thrust of a sudden squall, it does not need calculations to regain its equilibrium. Its reflexes come into action, and it balances quite instinctively. For the stability of my mechanical bird to be automatic, I wanted to give it a similar system of reflexes."

At this point, Verne sought to make use of his scientific intuition, which had made him world famous. Verne's invention consisted of a pylon fifteen feet high, which supported the two wings of his plane. Any side-to-side or up-and-down motion of the wings caused the pylon to react automatically. The free movement of the pylon brought into action weights that were free to slide parallel or perpendicular to the wings, which, in turn, warped the wings to correct any accidental oscillation. Thus, the wings were kept constantly balanced not only by the ailerons, flaps, vertical fins and rudders, but also by a gimbaled mast with its system of weights that reacted and moved automatically. The pilot was left with only the responsibility of steering the plane towards destination.

Verne thought of the future plane as a flying automaton. His imagination was groping towards the autopilot of today, which is accomplished by means of gyroscopes and electronic computers that eliminate the need for pilots to use control sticks, foot pedals and throttle controls. To prepare his readers, he quoted from Horace, "Do not be surprised at anything."

Verne's heliplane was powerful enough to travel without refueling up to 3,000 miles at an average speed of 250 miles an hour—a goal just being reached by rotary winged aircraft of today. A few years later, Verne's flying automaton took on new dimensions in *The Master of the World*. His new vehicle, the *Terrible*, is a bullet-shaped craft, capable of speeding on land, on water and under water, as well as through the air. Verne saw it as both a blessing and a threat.

The Birdmen

Langley's success with a powered flying model brought back the belief that a flying machine need only be made life-size to conquer the air. The American military advanced money for Langley to build the piloted machine.

The only barrier continued to be the light and powerful engine. Langley spent most of $100,000 he received from the government in trying to achieve a 100-pound gasoline engine that could deliver twelve horsepower. Manufacturers of engines in Europe and the United States informed him that it was impossible to build so light and powerful an engine. In the end, Langley's mechanic, Charles Manly, was forced to create one himself.

To eliminate the weight of water cooling, Manly placed the cylinders in a new star arrangement, mounted on a crankcase to get them air-cooled. The ignition system, carburetor and spark plugs had to be specially made. The final weight proved to be 207.5 pounds, but it delivered a surprising 52.4 horsepower and ran non-stop on three different tests of ten hours each. The weight-power ratio was 3.6 to 1.

On Aug. 8, 1903, Langley built a quarter-size counterpart

134

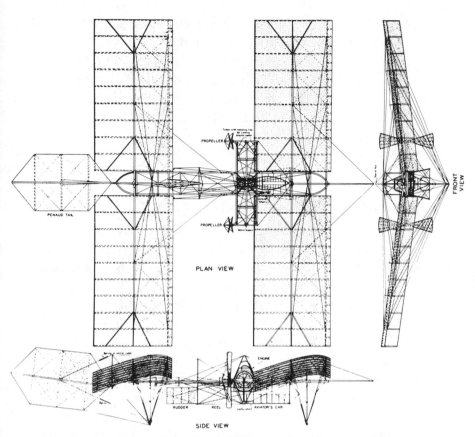

PROPELLER

PENAUD TAIL

PROPELLER

PLAN VIEW

FRONT VIEW

ENGINE

RUDDER   KEEL   AVIATOR'S CAR

SIDE VIEW

Plan for Aerodrome "A"—Samuel Pierpont Langley.
Smithsonian Institution.

of his "dragon-fly" machine. It flew directly ahead on an even
keel. It was the first successful flight of a mechanically sustained flying object ever to be made in public.

Langley felt confident that his full-size machine would be
equally successful. The launching gear on his houseboat on
the Potomac was eighty feet long and his tandem-winged airplane, resting on a turntable, could be swung to face the wind.
On the day of the test, two tugs full of reporters came to witness it. The *Aerodrome* was catapulted and flopped inglori-

ously into the water. After repairs it was launched again two months later, once more ducking the pilot into the Potomac. Since it was a secret army experiment, Langley had refused to admit newspaper men to his houseboat or shop, arousing their anger. The press hostility vented itself after the second failure, in ridicule of the starry-eyed professor. Congress, as a result, decided not to advance any more funds. It was a heart-breaking blow for the seventy-year-old scientist. He died soon after.

We know now that Langley's *Aerodrome* never could have succeeded in making a controlled flight even if the launching mechanism had worked perfectly. When the Smithsonian Institution permitted Glenn Curtiss to try it out again in 1914, he made thirty changes, supported it on floats, and succeeded only in achieving a series of short hops. Not even a light and powerful engine could get it airborne. For the few who understood, it dramatized the need for more aerodynamic research.

Only those few who risked their lives to fly on motorless gliders in the 1890's knew how really difficult it was to maintain stability and control while in the air. The press reported their activities on the sports page like a variation of the bicycle craze of that period. However, it was a dangerous sport, and the brave pioneers were fondly called "the birdmen." Very few people realized that these men's names would be engraved in history.

The birdmen first asked themselves what it was that was the secret of a bird's flight, as if to re-examine the phenomenon all over again. Like the radical painters of the modern art movement of that time, they sought to see an age-old problem with new eyes, going back to the beginning of things.

There was something new in their approach to their hobby. The wind was not to be attacked by brute force but won over by understanding. They all began by searching for wing forms that could coax the wind to lift them up just as it lifted the wings of birds. They knew about Captain Le Bris, who had detached a wing from an albatross to study it. When he had held it into the wind, he had had to push down with all his might to keep the wing from flying out of his hands.

It was Mouillard who had started the new wave of gliding with his book *The Empire of the Air*, published in 1886. He issued the call to amateurs to experiment with gliders rather than with balloons. They might break their necks, but the joys of skimming through the air made up for the danger.

The cambered wing was the first principle for all, although each modeled his wings on a different bird. Le Bris had copied the albatross. Mouillard preferred the vulture. John Montgomery began with the hen for short hops. Otto Lilienthal was first enamored with the stork. Chanute studied the buzzard. Pilcher selected the wing of the bat. The Wright brothers patterned theirs on the gull.

None of them had the monumental genius of a Cayley. All of them had to retrace his steps. In Hargrave's words, "By publishing and combining our efforts," they were able as a group to overtake Cayley and surpass the founding father. They proved to be as dedicated in searching for the secret of flight, as King Arthur's knights had been in seeking the Holy Grail.

The action really began with Otto Lilienthal (1848-1896), who at the age of thirteen, began trying to swoop down hillsides on homemade wings. He grew up to become a professional engineer, but he kept up his study of flight as a hobby. In 1889, he wrote a pamphlet called "The Flight of Birds as a Basis for the Art of Flying," emphasizing the curvature of the bird's wings as the lifting secret.

While Maxim and Ader were concentrating on the mechanical aspects of the flying machine, and other experimenters practiced on flying models, Lilienthal made a serious decision in 1891. He was weary of aeronautic papers and the endless spinning out of theories. "To conceive of a flying machine is nothing; to construct one is something, but to make a trial of it is everything." Lilienthal decided to soar over the chimney tops and the lakes of the countryside. He was forty-two years old, and he knew he would have to endure the jibes of his neighbors. He would be the only man in Europe to risk his neck so foolishly. But for him it was the only sensible thing to do. He would plunge with his glider from the rooftop of his home.

Otto and his brother Gustave built their glider in the shape of the wings of a bat, because they had the deepest curvature. The glider was lifted to the rooftop. Otto teetered on the edge. The wind was in the right direction, and the glider tugged upward against the flow as if to signal him to leap. He opened his eyes wide and sprang over the edge. Instead of flying over the countryside, he fell heavily to the ground below. Fortunately, the wings checked his fall and he did not break his legs. His life had been spared, he believed, to search out the secret of soaring.

If only he had had the designs and calculations of Cayley before him, he could have started where Cayley left off. Instead, there were years of struggle to retrace problems Cayley had already solved. Lilienthal had to experiment with different wing forms to determine which would best satisfy the basic needs. What dihedral offered the best stability? How much camber should the wing have to get the maximum lift? How much lift is needed to overcome a known amount of weight?

In his research, however, Lilienthal took a step beyond Cayley, for he piloted the gliders himself. In downhill hops he learned to secure a moderate amount of control by swinging his body towards the direction desired. Bamboo and cane ribs, curving upward, were attached to the coarse waxed cotton sails. They were braced by light willow rods, horizontal and transverse, on which Lilienthal could rest his arms and swing his dangling body to alter the position of the centers of pressure so as to have them coincide with the center of gravity.

In the flat countryside where Lilienthal lived, it was difficult to find a high enough elevation from which to leap with a glider. In 1893 he had a lucky break. A canal was being dug near his house, and he persuaded the canal builder to pile up the dirt in the middle of his field, creating a fifty-foot high jumping-off place, double the height that Cayley had recommended as a minimum for gliding.

In the year that Maxim was showing off his metal monster with its 5,000 square feet of surface, Lilienthal's machine seemed as small and fragile as a butterfly. Its batlike 18-foot span of wings had only 150 square feet of surface. When he flung himself and his glider from the top of the newly built mound, a gust of wind lifted them higher than the starting point. He landed safely about a hundred feet away. This was the first time that a glider had reached an altitude higher than the take-off point. Otto Lilienthal might rightfully be called the first man to soar.

He learned to prolong his flights from 100 to 400 feet. He became a skillful pilot, his shifting body counter-balancing the wings that were lifted up or pushed down slantwise by gusts of wind. He was beginning to learn how to make turns, hoping to return, like a boomerang, to his starting point.

"The way in which we experience the irregularities of the wind while gliding through the air cannot be learned in any other way except by being in the air itself," he said. He had his moments of glory as journalists and photographers flocked to his home to write up the sensational flying man. Pictures of Lilienthal flying through the air over the heads of spectators were reproduced in practically every paper around the world. He became the flying hero of the 1890's.

By 1896 Lilienthal realized that sustained flight would be impossible without a motor. He had noted that birds used the tips of their feathers for control and felt he was ready for motorized flapping wing flight. Like George Cayley, he decided that the air engine of the future would be powered by compressed air. He constructed a carbonic acid gas engine that had sufficient power to flap the ends of his wings. But he never tested it in action.

His flights had made him aware of the lack of lateral stability. He was testing a new horizontal steering arrangement for better control of the elevator when a sudden gust of wind sent him side-slipping into a fall that broke his back. As he lay dying, he gasped to his brother, "Sacrifices must be made." Gustave was broken by his brother's death and abandoned the dream of flying altogether.

"Sacrifices must be made." It was a call to others to continue the cause of flying. Lilienthal stirred the imagination of the aeronautic world. He had demonstrated that a soaring bird could be made of Mouillard's grasshopper glider. The world-wide publicity given Lilienthal and his martyrdom hardened the determination of the other birdmen to advance towards the conquest of the air.

It brought increased resolve to Octave Chanute, who had made himself the mouthpiece of the half dozen men who were risking their lives to discover the secret of equilibrium. The retired, wealthy engineer had written a book, *Progress in Flying Machines* in 1894, organized conferences, outlined goals for the future.

However, most of the men who contributed papers to Chanute's international conferences were theoreticians, who devoted themselves to laboratory experiments with models. Étienne-Jules Marey, for example, had worked out methods of stop-photography to study the maneuvering of birds in the wind. The photographs proved that feathers served as both lift and propulsion, wing and propeller. The tails of birds were used as flaps to slow down speed. Feathers opened up to get the air to flow faster to increase speed. Wings worked separately to keep flight level in gusty winds. The aeronauts

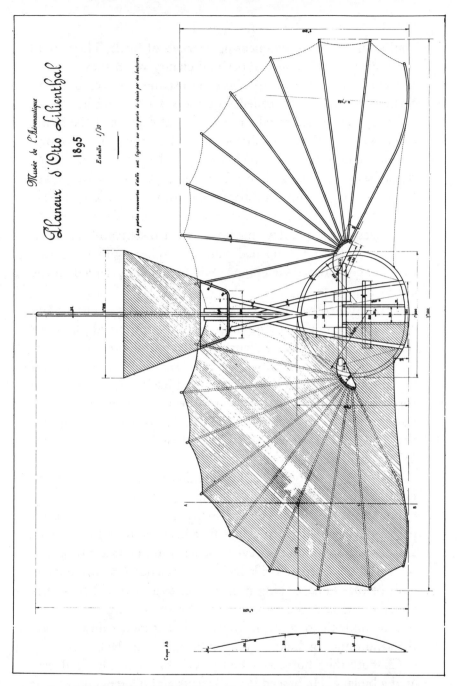

Glider of Otto Lilienthal, 1895. *Smithsonian Institution.*

could only envy the engineering marvels of birds. They could not hope to emulate such superb efficiency when they had not yet even learned how to make a sustained powered flight. Something more was needed, but no one knew what.

Everyone seemed to take the imminent success of the flying machine for granted, only to find that the golden shore, within sight, vanished like a mirage. Hargraves, from Australia, sent in papers describing his experiments to power flying box kites with compressed air, firework rockets, clockwork devices. He claimed that a metal tube with compressed air, released as a jet, flew his box kites a distance of 312 feet. Augustus Herring, who had piloted Cayley's glider, hurried to try a compressed air engine. His failure only added to the confusion.

When Lilienthal died, Chanute was past sixty, but he decided that he must now be more than a theoretician; he must fill the gap created by Lilienthal's death and become a birdman himself. For the time being at least, he saw no need of any motive power outside of the wind itself. He had seen the force of the wind cause a glider to hover at one point, motionless as a hawk, for minutes at a time. He began with a glider that had a dozen superposed wings, based on one created by Wenham in 1866.

On the sand dunes of Lake Michigan, with all sails spread on its canoe-shaped frame, Chanute's glider had the look of a clipper ship of the air. It had many unique features. Its six pairs of wings of light silk had first been saturated in a preparation of guncotton to prevent penetration of water or air. A width of this prepared silk had been extended to the outside ends of the frame, hoping it might act as a kind of keel to the aerial craft, and thus give it greater safety. But the glider proved difficult to control. Many a time it swept downhill on the sand dunes of Lake Michigan and into the lake itself.

Chanute then borrowed Hargrave's box-kite idea and created a biplane. He braced it with struts and diagonal wires that added little weight, but made it more sturdy and efficient. He reduced the weight to thirty-six pounds and the wings to fifteen feet long by fourteen feet wide. But with all these efforts, Chanute could not get his glider to go much beyond Lilienthal's four hundred feet. Nor would it soar above thirty feet. The secret of sustained flight was still wrapped in an enigma.

He felt that it might be possible to create some kind of automatic device that could take the place of shifting the weight of the dangling body, which had proved to be exhausting. So he constructed a lever that moved the wings forward and backward to control the drifting centers of pressure. This, he thought, might combine Langley's flying automaton with

Chanute flying one of his gliders.
Smithsonian Institution.

Lilienthal's faith in the skill of a pilot.

He was too old, himself, to go ahead with any prolonged experimentation, and he looked to younger men for further improvements. There was Percy Pilcher in England, who built his first glider in 1893 when he was twenty-seven years old. The young engineer wanted a wing that could support a pound weight to every half-square-foot, and large enough to be capable of carrying two hundred pounds including his own weight. Pilcher built four different models, which he named "Bat," "Beetle," "Gull" and "Hawk."

After a visit to Lilienthal in 1895, Pilcher followed his advice to reduce the v-shaped camber of his wings to give them a curve of only one in twenty, with the apex about one-third from the front. He laced these treated silk wings to a triangle of heavy spars, guyed to two uprights. A small vertical rudder was to keep the machine head-on to the wind, while a horizontal worked up and down over it, something new in the arrangement of the tailpiece. He placed his glider on two small bicycle wheels to give it a swifter flying start.

Each succeeding model weighed more. The first was forty-five pounds, the fourth, built in 1898, 250 pounds. The later one had a three-quarter square foot wing area to the pound weight, enough to carry both man and engine.

With this glider, Pilcher sailed 900 feet across a valley from hilltop to hilltop, to break the world record for glider flight. He felt himself ready to place an engine on his glider, and he had begun work on a gasoline engine. One August day, crowds of visitors came to see the fantastic spectacle of a soaring leap across a valley. After a heavy rain, to please the Sunday crowd, he mounted his glider to cross the valley. He had reached the midpoint of his flight when one of the rudder guys snapped. The glider toppled forward and sideways and Pilcher plunged to his death. His tragic end eliminated the very real possibility that he might have made the first airplane flight.

Where was the glider man to take Pilcher's place? It required years of practice to learn the art, and it seemed to Chanute at that moment that there was no one to hold aloft the torch of the last fallen comrade. He had no faith in Langley's flying automaton, which was still being built. How strange that Chanute should have received a letter from two unknowns asking for glider information at a time when the art seemed to have reached a dead end! The letter was from the Wright brothers and it came at a fateful moment.

The Secret of Flight

Science fiction writers could only speculate about the missing link that would make flight possible. The finest engineering brains in the world had experimented and failed. A century of effort and the expenditure of millions had not solved the enigma. But the time was ripe. The Wright brothers were at work.

Their father had planted the seed by giving his sons a toy model of Penaud's planophore. The half-minute flight of this mechanical bird fascinated them with the wonders of mechanics. They dropped out of school to earn their living in the joyous task of creating and selling mechanical toys. The profits were invested in a bicycle business, which prospered. Though they were largely self taught, they became skilled mechanics.

The tragic death of Otto Lilienthal turned their thoughts back to their mechanical bird. Flight had always fascinated them. After an all night discussion, they decided to throw themselves into the gap left by the death of Lilienthal.

They wrote immediately to the Smithsonian Institution for advice on the study of aeronautics. The librarian replied with

146

a list of books that included: Étienne Marey's *Animal Mechanisms*, Mouillard's *Empire of the Air*, Lilienthal's *Experiments in Soaring*, Langley's *Story of Experiments in Mechanical Flight and Experiments in Aerodynamics*, Chanute's *Progress in Flying Machines*.

Letter of Wilbur Wright to the Smithsonian Institution. *Smithsonian Institution.*

Their studies proved to be an exciting theoretical adventure . . . a search for an elusive villain, the concealed secret of flight. George Cayley had almost hit the mark a hundred years earlier. But Cayley had launched his gliders in still air. Chanute had insisted that man would have to learn how to keep a glider in equipoise through constantly changing wind pressures. And the brothers could see that he was right.

They were surprised to learn how little time Lilienthal and Pilcher had spent in actual gliding. Altogether, as Orville was to later write, "We were astounded to learn what an immense amount of time and money had been expended in futile attempts to solve the problem of flight." A host of experimenters had grasped some part of the truth, but failed to perceive the whole truth of how a glider could be made stable in the air. And part of their trouble had been a lack of experience with the air itself.

When Pilcher plunged to his death in 1899, the Wrights were further moved. They felt they shared something of the spirit of Pilcher, and they wrote to Chanute of their decision, even if it meant death, to launch themselves in a glider. They asked for information on how to build one. Chanute, who was known for his sweetness and idealism, realized at once that the Wright brothers were kindred spirits. He answered promptly.

They were ready now, after two years of study and with Chanute's plans, to translate theory into action. They built a five-foot model of Chanute's biplane and flew it as a kite to test its stability. They manipulated special ropes that controlled the horizontal and vertical tail surfaces to prevent a nose dive, but it was difficult to keep the glider level. One wing would always be lower or higher than the other. They saw, at once, why Lilienthal and Pilcher had kept their gliders in balance only by shifting the weight of their bodies. Obviously, something new would have to be added for lateral stability.

They knew of Chanute's automatic regulator, which moved

the wings forward and backward, but it could not have the same instantaneous response of the dangling pilot. Was there no better way than to swing like a pendulum? The brothers argued and theorized. One thing was certain. The shape of the wings needed constant change to keep the equilibrium. All flapping-wing experiments had failed. Another way must be found to change the shape of the wings while they were in the air.

Like many others, they decided to study the ways of birds. Through field glasses, Orville observed how buzzards were rocked to one side by a gust of wind, but righted themselves by dropping one wing and lifting the other. Looking more sharply, he became aware of an almost imperceptible new movement, the twisting of the tips of their wings. As the tip of one feather went up, its diagonal opposite went down.

Here was something that others had overlooked. The birds moved the entire wing only in heavy winds. Normally, a change in the tips of feathers was sufficient. In a flash, Orville grasped the idea that if a pilot could give one wing tip of a glider more lift than the other, he would be able to give his glider lateral stability. No glider pilot they knew of had attempted to do this.

Historians today know that Matthew Boulton in England had patented a small movable wing tip, a hinged aileron, as far back as 1868. When Penaud patented a similar arrangement in the next decade, he was unaware of the English patent. By the time Orville came upon the idea, both English and French patents lay dusty and forgotten in old archives. Their owners were dead and patent rights had lapsed.

Wilbur, who was the creative mechanic, pondered all kinds of devices. Most mechanical arrangements so increased the weight of the wing as to cancel their efficiency. He was puzzled and vexed by the problem for months. Strangely enough, the solution came to him with an odd flash of insight similar to the one that Edison had experienced with the problem of his lamp filament. Edison had been twisting a loose thread on his suit when the idea popped into his head that he could carbonize the thread and make a filament of it.

Wilbur was twisting a cardboard box nervously in his shop, while a customer was examining an innertube. Suddenly, he became aware that twisting his box at diagonal ends did no damage to the inherent strength of the box. Why couldn't a biplane glider be warped at the diagonal tips by means of wires arranged as a shoulder harness on a pilot as he lay prone on a glider? By shifting the shoulders, one wing tip could be made to go down and the other up, simultaneously.

The more Wilbur thought of the idea, the more excited he became. He felt he had discovered the missing link to the mystery of air flight. Now he had the key to simultaneous control in three axes in space: he could go up or down by manipulating an elevator with his right hand; swing right or left by using his left hand to control the rudder; and achieve lateral balance against any sudden gust of wind or on making a turn simply by swinging his shoulders to warp the wing tips. The concept worked perfectly when they tested it on their model glider. The real proof, however, would have to come by testing a man-carrying glider.

They were ready now to launch themselves in the air. They built their first manned glider on the basis of Lilienthal's tables of air pressures. Lilienthal had warned against using too deep a curvature. The deepest portion of the curve should be well forward towards the leading edge of the wing, but the curve (or camber) as a whole, should have the ratio of about one to twelve.

To be on the safe side, Wilbur placed the horizontal surface of the elevator in front instead of making it a part of the tail-piece. Lying prone on the center of the lower wing, he could keep a sharp eye on the horizontal surface out front and move quickly to prevent a sudden nose dive. He asked the weather bureau in Washington for the safest place for gliding and learned that the steadiest, all-year-round winds were to be found on the shores of North Carolina. The soft sand would make any crash comparatively painless.

The two storekeepers crated their glider and went off to Kitty Hawk during the Christmas holiday. Looking for the right place to work, they found a gently sloping, 100-foot sand dune, known as Kill Devil Hill. Once they began flying their glider, they found they had a devil of a time keeping it steady. Most of their time was spent in making changes and testing the glider as a kite in winds of different speeds. The problem of controlling a seventeen-foot glider still remained unsolved when they had to hurry home to attend to business.

They built their second glider in 1901 with a wing area of 290 square feet, and a span of 22 feet. When Wilbur, in the summer of that year, flung himself over Kill Devil Hill on it, the center of pressure near the front of the wings began mov-

A Wright glider being flown.
Smithsonian Institution.

ing rapidly backward. He had to pitch himself forward a full foot to drive the center of pressure forward again.

The lifting power of this second glider was not as good as they had hoped it would be. They decided, after a long discussion, that the fault lay in the camber of the wing, which they changed from one to twelve to one to twenty. With this lesser curve, Wilbur succeeded in gliding up to 389 feet. However, when he warped the wings with his harness, the glider sideslipped and hit the ground.

Fortunately, Chanute paid them a visit that summer of 1901. He admired their glider and congratulated them on having made the best one so far. The sideslipping, he said, could only be blamed on wrong air pressure tables. It was possible that Lilienthal's tables might not be too accurate. Chanute persuaded Wilbur to deliver a speech on his progress at the annual meeting of the Western Society of Engineers in Chicago.

Wilbur's speech in Chicago startled the aeronautic world. He explained his warping technique, and he expressed doubts about the pressure tables in general use. In one sense, it was an attack on Langley, who was building a full-size plane for the War Department and was using the standard tables of that time.

With the publication of his speech, Wilbur became aware of the fact that he was no longer merely pursuing a hobby. He was recognized as the peer of serious scientists. And as Wilbur had suspected he would, Chanute began pleading with him to calculate a more accurate series of measurements for pressure tables. About 2,000 measurements demanded to be tested. Wilbur had to put aside his real ambition, which was to build another glider, and go ahead with this tedious operation.

The Wright brothers were not rich, and they were forced to use whatever tools were available to them. For their wind tunnel, they built a rectangular box through which they could pass an artificial wind. Since they had no electricity with which to turn a fan, the brothers had to improvise. They connected a one-cylinder gasoline engine to a spindle from an emery wheel and with that turned an electric fan.

Then they cut out tiny, sheet metal wings of more than two hundred shapes and sizes. Month after month, in whatever moments they could spare from their business, they tabulated the lifting power of these miniature wings. They tested more than 50 surfaces at angles from zero to 45 degrees at intervals of 2.5 degrees. They gave their wings thicker and thinner leading edges. They tried out superimposed wings in the forms of biplanes and triplanes and even placed wings in tandem, as Langley was doing. They changed their lengths and widths and curves. They worked on their tables from September 1901 to August of 1902.

When the tabulations of lift were completed, they proved to be different from those published earlier. Among other surprises, the Wrights had learned that a single surface was most efficient; but they decided on a biplane because of its sturdiness. They were in a position now to predict the behavior of different lengths, widths and curves in an aircraft. They felt the elation of knowing that they were the only ones in the world who had crossed a new frontier towards the conquest of the skies.

Their third glider, which they built in September of 1902, had a greater span than ever—32 feet, with 305 square feet of surface. A five foot width gave the wings the shape of gull wings. The curvature was reduced to one in thirty. It was the kind of plane that could be controlled only by a skillful pilot.

The Wright brothers were not seeking to achieve an inherently stable plane. They realized that there was not enough knowledge about the circulation of air around a wing to make this possible. They wanted only to achieve a plane that would allow them to rely on their skill in handling control surfaces.

Although their measurements were more accurate than any

in use before, they still had to proceed on a trial and error basis. Because of the greater size of their 1902 glider, they decided to have two fixed vertical rudders in the rear. They hoped they could counteract in this way the one great difficulty that had plagued them whenever they warped their wings—the tendency to spin and crash. The Kitty Hawk trials that summer proved that the double rear fins only increased the windmill spin. So, then and there, they changed the fixed twin rudders into a single movable one. After this change, at the moment of warping, the pilot could swing the one rudder to the right position to correct exaggerated tilt when making a turn, and then reverse the swing to redirect the plane.

This new arrangement worked beautifully. At last, they were able to make smooth, banked turns. They made hundreds of perfectly controlled glides, setting a distance record of 622.5 feet in 26 seconds.

By this time improvements were coming rapidly. Orville suggested the possibility of a single control that would connect the wings tips to the movable rudder. Such a co-ordination gave the pilot a free hand to use the front control surfaces at the same time if necessary. Wilbur connected the wires to a simple lever. They had, finally, achieved the arrangement that would earn for them the basic patent rights four years later.

By the end of that summer, the Wrights felt they had mastered the glider. They had a system of balances effective in winds as well as in calms. They understood how a glider could be balanced in the air as surely as ships are balanced in water. They were the first human beings privileged to glimpse the true mathematical secret of stable flight in windy weather. They, alone, had the adaptive mechanisms and the skill to make a glider behave as they wanted it to. Many times they escaped disaster by the instant swinging of their levers or their hip cradle. They felt themselves the only aeronauts who had the experience and the knowledge to cope with the blows and shocks of the wind.

Their new-found knowledge explains why they did not join in the world-wide excitement over the great Langley experiment. No automatic device at that early stage of technology could be as foolproof as the eternal vigilance of the pilot, they realized. The Wright brothers were the first of the birdmen who were truly ready for powered flight.

The Phantom Biplane

W<small>HEN THEY RETURNED TO</small> D<small>AYTON, THE</small> W<small>RIGHTS FELT SO</small>
certain of success that they applied for a patent on their warp-
ing device. Before building their new powered glider, which
they already named the *Flyer*, they had to tackle the problem
of the engine. No gasoline engine had ever been built for a
heavier-than-air machine.

George Cayley, who had had the genius to penetrate to the
heart of the problem, had called such an engine a heat engine.
He had written eloquently of the future engine, of a heat flow
greater than steam. He pictured the blazing interior of its
inner chamber below a piston that would keep exploding injected fuel in rapid, tremendous thrusts of power. Connecting
rods, attached to the piston, would transmit these bursts of
force to the crankshaft, kicking it into a rotating motion for
useful work in swinging flappers or rotating propellers.

Engineers in Europe and the United States had told Langley
that a weight-power ratio of 2.5 to 1 for an airplane engine
was an impossibility. The Wright brothers had no such miracle of engine design in mind when they tackled their engine.
What they achieved was an engine with a weight-power ratio

of about seven to one.

The Wrights were fortunate in that they were the first aeronauts to find cheap machine parts and fuel available. The cheap manufacture of aluminum had begun in 1896. The 1900 Spindletop gusher in Texas had reduced the price of gasoline. Steel tubing, wire cables and storage batteries had become abundant. The Wrights tore an automobile engine apart and reassembled it, substituting lightweight aluminum parts wherever feasible. They tried more than a dozen different arrangements. Finally, they had a four-inch stroke that gave them 12 horsepower at 1,025 revolutions a minute. It was a 240 pound power unit, just about capable of propelling a 750 pound aircraft at thirty miles an hour. A strong enough wind should be capable of lifting it off the ground.

The inventors of the airplane took equal pains in shaping their first propeller. The Wrights understood that the air propeller should be designed according to their aerodynamic tables. A propeller was simply a wing traveling a spiral course. They studied their tables to give it the proper diameter, the best area of blade, the right pitch. They kept reshaping it until they succeeded in giving it, in useful work, two thirds of the power expended. A staccato clacking told them when it was working at peak. They decided to use two propellers circling in opposite directions to balance the twisting effect that one rear propeller would bring.

By this time they were in a position to calculate the dimensions of their *Flyer*. They worked with such precision, they figured that the weight of the engine, right of center, would be 34 pounds more than the pilot who would be lying beside it, left of center. Thus they had to make their right wing four inches longer to provide additional lifting power for their engine weight. Altogether, the wings spanned forty feet and four inches.

Every schoolboy knows of the one minute flight at Kitty

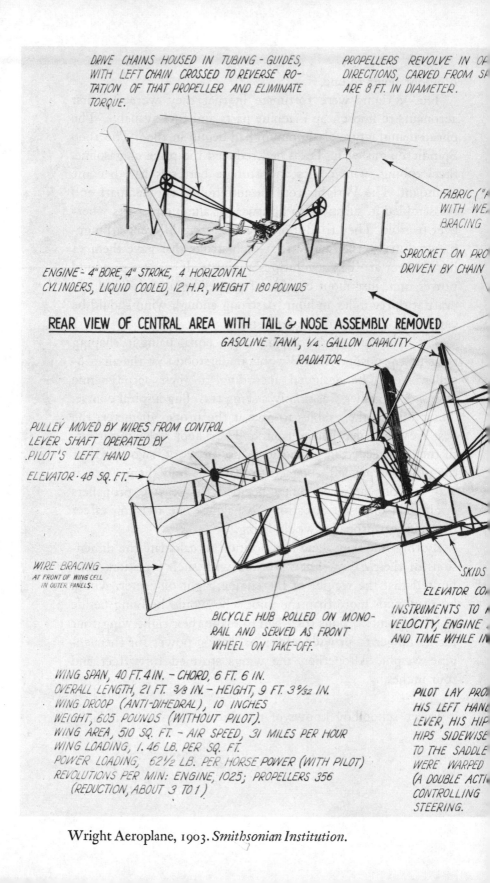

DRIVE CHAINS HOUSED IN TUBING - GUIDES,
WITH LEFT CHAIN CROSSED TO REVERSE RO-
TATION OF THAT PROPELLER AND ELIMINATE
TORQUE.

PROPELLERS REVOLVE IN OF
DIRECTIONS, CARVED FROM S
ARE 8 FT. IN DIAMETER.

FABRIC ("
WITH WE
BRACING

SPROCKET ON PRO
DRIVEN BY CHAIN

ENGINE - 4" BORE, 4" STROKE, 4 HORIZONTAL
CYLINDERS, LIQUID COOLED, 12 H.P., WEIGHT 180 POUNDS

REAR VIEW OF CENTRAL AREA WITH TAIL & NOSE ASSEMBLY REMOVED

GASOLINE TANK, 1/4 GALLON CAPACITY
RADIATOR

PULLEY MOVED BY WIRES FROM CONTROL
LEVER SHAFT OPERATED BY
PILOT'S LEFT HAND

ELEVATOR · 48 SQ. FT.

WIRE BRACING
AT FRONT OF WING CELL
IN OUTER PANELS.

SKIDS

ELEVATOR CO

INSTRUMENTS TO
VELOCITY, ENGINE
AND TIME WHILE IN

BICYCLE HUB ROLLED ON MONO-
RAIL AND SERVED AS FRONT
WHEEL ON TAKE-OFF.

WING SPAN, 40 FT. 4 IN. - CHORD, 6 FT. 6 IN.
OVERALL LENGTH, 21 FT. 3/8 IN. - HEIGHT, 9 FT. 3 9/32 IN.
WING DROOP (ANTI-DIHEDRAL), 10 INCHES
WEIGHT, 605 POUNDS (WITHOUT PILOT).
WING AREA, 510 SQ. FT. - AIR SPEED, 31 MILES PER HOUR
WING LOADING, 1.46 LB. PER SQ. FT.
POWER LOADING, 62 1/2 LB. PER HORSE POWER (WITH PILOT)
REVOLUTIONS PER MIN: ENGINE, 1025; PROPELLERS 356
(REDUCTION, ABOUT 3 TO 1)

PILOT LAY PRO
HIS LEFT HAND
LEVER, HIS HIP
HIPS SIDEWISE
TO THE SADDLE
WERE WARPED
(A DOUBLE ACTI
CONTROLLING
STEERING.

Wright Aeroplane, 1903. *Smithsonian Institution.*

WRIGHT AEROPLANE, 1903
NOMENCLATURE & DETAILS

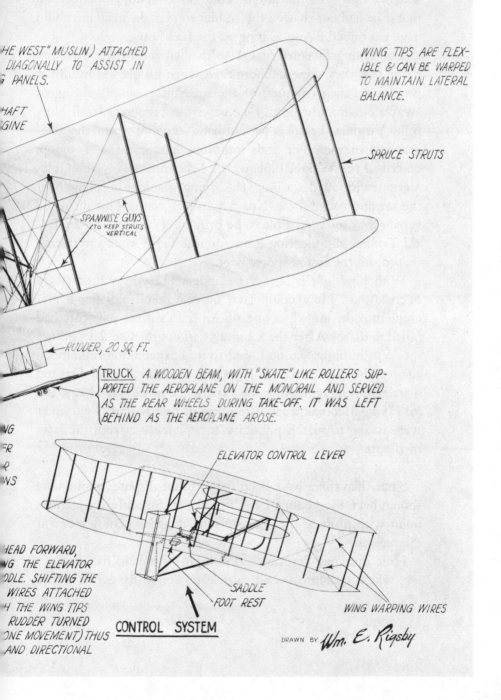

HE WEST." MUSLIN) ATTACHED
DIAGONALLY TO ASSIST IN
G PANELS.

HAFT
GINE

WING TIPS ARE FLEX-
IBLE & CAN BE WARPED
TO MAINTAIN LATERAL
BALANCE.

SPRUCE STRUTS

SPANWISE GUYS
TO KEEP STRUTS
VERTICAL

RUDDER, 20 SQ. FT.

TRUCK A WOODEN BEAM, WITH "SKATE" LIKE ROLLERS SUP-
PORTED THE AEROPLANE ON THE MONORAIL AND SERVED
AS THE REAR WHEELS DURING TAKE-OFF. IT WAS LEFT
BEHIND AS THE AEROPLANE AROSE.

NG
FR
R
NS

ELEVATOR CONTROL LEVER

HEAD FORWARD,
NG THE ELEVATOR
DDLE. SHIFTING THE
WIRES ATTACHED
H THE WING TIPS
RUDDER TURNED
ONE MOVEMENT) THUS
AND DIRECTIONAL

SADDLE
FOOT REST

CONTROL SYSTEM

WING WARPING WIRES

DRAWN BY *Wm. E. Rigsby*

Hawk. The spirits of Leonardo Da Vinci and George Cayley, Henson and Penaud, Ader and Maxim were there. The Wright glider had been transformed into the *Flyer,* and it actually flew. On the last of four tests, Wilbur was certain that if he had not twisted the rudder too far the machine could have continued flying as long as the fuel lasted.

The young inventors were so thrilled with their own triumph that they were flabbergasted when no blazing headlines proclaimed their conquest of the air. Editors simply shrugged away a one-minute flight. One newspaper reporter from Norfolk, Virginia, heard a second-hand account from the telegraph operator. The cub reporter, hungry for a scoop, described the Wright biplane as a helicopter and gave a Jules Verne twist by describing the flying machine circling over the sea and back to the North Carolina coast. This distorted version was too incredible to be printed. *The New York Herald Tribune* did mention a one-minute flight as an interesting record, on the inside sports page.

With hindsight it is easy to understand why editors were overcautious. How could two bicycle mechanics get a machine into the air when one of America's great scientists had failed to do so? After the Langley fiasco, just nine days before the Wright flight, a mood of shattered expectation rebounded against the "upstarts." The young mechanics from Dayton were simply exaggerating the experience of *Darius Green and his Flying Machine,* a favorite poem of that period. Two hicks were trying to snatch publicity for themselves from the jaws of disaster.

Since then there have been many bitter disputes about who should have the honor of the first flight. Six different nations point with pride at their native sons and claim the honor for themselves.

How does one describe a first flight? England has its Cayley, whose coachman used muscle power to fly across a dale in 1853. Du Temple of France, in 1859, and Mozhaiski of Russia, lifted a plane with the help of gravity power provided by a ramp. Ader's 1890 *Éole* had a steam engine with a little more than a three to one weight-power ratio, and lifted off the ground for a few feet, but his plane had no control.

It is true that the Wright brothers used a detachable trolley to give their *Flyer* a skidding start. The trolley was a six-foot plank with two small wheels, one behind the other. They had a track of wood covered with greased sheet-iron strips. On the historic day of December 17, 1903, a twenty-seven mile per hour wind lifted their powered glider four feet in the air before it reached the end of the track. The trolley was left behind. And no one can deny that Wilbur started his flight at ten miles per hour and reached a speed of thirty miles per hour with his engine. The pilot kept his flight stable by controlling his surfaces against heavy gusts and wind shifts, until a mistaken movement of the rudder reduced height too quickly. The anemometer and stopwatch on the plane recorded 852 feet in 59 seconds.

Back in Dayton the brothers knew they had taken only the first of a thousand steps needed to reach practical flight. They built their second *Flyer* in May of 1904. For this they set up an air field on a ninety-acre pasture about eight miles east of Dayton. Their new engine developed 16 horsepower, but was not powerful enough to lift them off the ground without help of the wind. They were able to make flights to learn how to control and maneuver a powered machine only on windy days.

They spent an entire summer building a weight and derrick catapult device to make them independent of the weather. The area of the pasture was just large enough for circular flights, but the tight turns caused their plane to lose speed to the danger point of stalling. Fortunately, Wilbur knew enough aerodynamics to gain speed by turning down the nose while turning. This bit of knowledge saved his life on more than one occasion.

Once again, he had bad luck with the press. A dozen reporters came from different parts of the country to confirm the rumors that "Darius Green" had a flying machine that could fly. As many as fifty spectators gathered to watch the demonstration. On the first occasion, the Wright brothers were unable to start the engine. The other time, the engine stalled and brought the plane to a skidding stop. Was it possible they wanted no publicity? Were they so absorbed in perfecting their plane that they preferred to work quietly and in secret? If so, they succeeded, for the reporters left in disgust, and the press maintained a dignified silence about them for the next four years. The Wright *Flyer* in the popular imagination became a phantom biplane.

There was one exception. The proprietor and editor of a local trade paper, *The Gleanings on Bee Culture*, arrived on September 20, 1904, to interview the sons of Bishop Wright. It was the day when Wilbur made the first full circle flight. The amazed editor wrote, "When it first turned that circle and came near the starting point, I was right in front of it . . . it was . . . the grandest sight of my life . . . imagine a locomotive that has left its track and is climbing up in the air right towards you." The eye-witness account never reached the rest of the press.

On November 17, 1904, the Wrights succeeded at last in making a five-minute flight.

Sensational progress was made in 1905. For the first time the Wrights had a truly practical airplane. Improved fuel injection gave their engine 20 horsepower and increased their speed to 38 miles per hour. To improve longitudinal control, they placed the elevators further forward, and the rudder further back. The curve of their wings was increased from the 1 to 30 camber to a deeper 1 to 20 camber. They found it was more useful to separate the warp and rudder controls, so as to give the pilot greater freedom to use them separately, or in combination, in any desired degree. With these changes Wilbur was able to circle and even make figure eights.

The record speaks for itself: September 26th, a flight of 11 miles; September 30th, 12 miles; October 3rd, 15 miles; October 4th, 20 miles; October 5th, 24 miles. There were no official observers, only a passing trolley car, whose passengers strained their necks to see the weird goings-on. For the Wright brothers, it was a success beyond their dreams, accomplished, it seemed, overnight.

They had not yet received their patents, but they sensed that they had become important. They were no longer small-time bicycle manufacturers. They were the sole possessors of a successful airplane, with possibilities of world patent rights. They could become the world monopolists of the most important invention of mankind.

A dizzying prospect opened up of vast riches with royalties pouring in from every military establishment around the earth. They came to a quick decision. They had been in business long enough to know all about pirates, infringements and spies. Their invention might suffer the fate of Whitney's cotton gin, which came into such quick and universal use no one felt obliged to pay any royalties. Too many inventors had been victimized by unscrupulous promoters. The only certain protection for them was secrecy.

They stored their planes in a barn and locked the door. The trolley-riders near Dayton would not see a plane fly again for another decade. The Wrights, themselves, were not to fly again until three years later. As far as the public knew, they had vanished into the obscurity of failure. Actually they were building three new *Flyers* and experimenting with the engine in the hope that it might be made powerful enough to lift their plane off the ground in windless weather. A great deal of time was spent in written negotiations with military authorities.

During three years of non-flight their sole aim was to get a down payment and a firm contract. They needed the money badly. They had abandoned all hope of getting such a contract from their own country. The United States Army was not interested in purchasing an airplane.

European nations, however, were sitting on a powder keg, and their war departments wrote back for permission to send observers for a demonstration flight. The Wrights insisted on a signed contract first. The French sent a Captain Ferber, but the inventors refused to show their plane unless the French first agreed to buy it for a quarter-million dollars. The tug of war continued for years, only to further discredit the claims of the brothers.

Their friend, Octave Chanute, was dismayed by their attitude. He warned them that the French were going ahead with serious experiments and might discover the secret of flight any day. Chanute had spoken before the French Aero Club in the Spring of 1903, disclosing the Wright technique to maintain lateral stability. The French aeronauts had heard that "the operator works two cords which warp the right and left wing and at the same time adjusts the vertical rear rudder." The speech launched the French aeronauts into gliding.

The Wrights knew there was more to flight than theoretical explanations. No one could learn how to fly without devoting the years of practice that they had done. They had a five year start, and they could afford to wait. The army that wanted their plane could get it only on a cash-and-carry basis.

Nor were they seriously disturbed by other glider flights. Unaware of what the Wrights had accomplished, other birdmen in different countries were continuing glider experiments. Ever since 1883 a professor at Santa Clara College, John Montgomery had made gliding his hobby, aiming for the flapping wing flight of George Cayley. He learned to use

Montgomery with his glider. *Smithsonian Institution.*

flaps at the end of his wings in a new way. They were held in place by light springs, so that any excessive gust of wind would push them down and restore the equilibrium of the glider.

In 1904 Daniel Maloney, a daring parachute jumper, made free flight exhibitions of Montgomery's new glider, in which the dihedral cambered wings were placed in tandem, one pair behind the other. Maloney made many jumps in it from balloons, exhibiting breath-taking skill with sharp turns, spirals, figure eights and hair-raising dives. Alexander Graham Bell, the inventor of the telephone and also an aeronautic expert, who had backed up Langley, stated, "All subsequent attempts in aviation must begin with the Montgomery machine."

Wilbur Wright studied the design in Montgomery's pamphlet, and shook his head in dismay. He expressed his warning to Chanute that the tandem arrangement was dangerous. In a 1905 exhibition, a wing was damaged, and the glider spun

over and dropped upside down, killing the pilot, Maloney. Disregarding Wright's warning, Montgomery himself fell to his death in 1911.

It was their understanding of the weakness of other aerodynamic designs that gave the Wright brothers the complete confidence that they had no real competition.

It took three years for the United States Patent Office to reach a conclusion about the Wright invention. Warping the wing tips and swinging the rear rudders might seem to be an insignificant method to attain stability. And yet the scientists in the Patent Office had to admit that such movements made all the difference in maintaining balance in gusty winds. The Wrights had hit upon a true secret of stability. Others might use other methods, but in all fairness, they would have to admit the basic idea originated with the Wrights. Patent No. 831,393 was granted them, finally, on May 22, 1906.

They applied for patents in all the European countries in their drive to control world-wide rights. However, the expected flood of orders did not materialize. Nor did the inventors agree to the continued requests for a demonstration flight before European military observers. It was the old story of the pot and the kettle calling each other black. To one, the American mechanics were bluffing; to the other, the military wanted to spy out a secret, without paying for it.

A young man in England, A. V. Roe, who was destined to fly the first plane in that country, became convinced that the twenty-four mile flight was a fact. The Wrights were too well known among air enthusiasts for the advances they had made in gliders to risk their honor in a false report. Roe protested to *The London Times* in 1906 that no publicity had been given the greatest achievement of the time. Why should not a motor-driven aeroplane develop great speeds with comparatively small power, since the Wrights were even capable of moving against the wind without running the engine?

Such an air transport, it seemed to him, should have a greater future than a cigar-shaped balloon which offered so large a resistance to the wind.

The engineering editor of *The Times* dismissed the logic as absurd. "Such artificial aviation," he wrote, "was not only dangerous to human life but was foredoomed to failure from an engineering standpoint." A few months later, in the Autumn of 1906, Santos Dumont launched a demonstration flight of his *Infuriated Grasshopper* before a crowd of spectators and reporters. In two different flights, he proved that he could lift a heavier-than-air machine from the ground. Never did an airman receive such multitudinous applause and homage. As Chanute had predicted, the palm of victory was given to a Frenchman. Another had stolen the glory that rightfully should have been given to the Wright brothers.

The Angel of the Revolution

On Alberto Santos Dumont's first balloon flight in the air he had the peculiar sense that he had entered the future. The entire world became absolutely new and strange. Not the balloon, but the earth was in flight, plunging down away from him. He saw the black shadow of his balloon against a triple rainbow. When landing, railroad, village and woods rushed towards him with frightening velocity. It took only one trip to galvanize him, heart and soul, to the study of ballooning. At once, he lost all interest in the auto races in which he had competed with other rich sportsmen. He dreamed of possessing the smallest possible steerable balloon, which he could use as an aerial taxi to go from place to place at his pleasure.

The young millionaire sportsman, not yet twenty-five, began by ordering the smallest balloon in the world for his personal use. Despite objections, he insisted that the bag be made of varnished Japanese silk instead of the usual heavy treated taffetas. Santos revealed his genius when he proved that the lighter Japanese silk was stronger than the conventional heavy material.

The tiny balloon was no sooner built and flown than he decided to construct an equally tiny dirigible that could be steered against the wind with the new automobile engine. By 1898, the weight-power ratio of the gasoline engine had been reduced from 88 pounds per horsepower to 20 pounds. But would the vibrations of the engine shake an aircraft to pieces? Santos tested everything that might cause trouble, and so he tested the motor vibrations. He slung a motorcycle over a low-hanging limb of a tree and climbed onto the driver's seat. Since the engine had nothing to vibrate against, it ran more smoothly than on the ground.

His next step was to build a cigar-shaped bag that would offer less resistance to the wind than a balloon. Below the bag he built a long catwalk; by running up and down the catwalk, he could use his own weight to keep the balloon balanced in the air. A sandbag trolley was included to give added weight if this should be necessary. A large triangular rudder over a wire frame was designed to swing the bag from one direction to another. An inner ballonet was included in the balloon itself. This could be blown up with a bicycle pump as hydrogen was lost, in order to preserve the dirigible shape.

At last, in 1899, when the Wright brothers began building their first glider, Santos had the smallest powered airship ever built ready for testing. His friends condemned him for embarking on a suicide project. A German, Wolfert, had burned to death in the wire-cage of his benzine-powered dirigible. A Russian aluminum monster had blown to bits in St. Petersburg. They cited others who had lost their lives when their internal combustion engines set the hydrogen on fire.

Santos argued that dirigibles in the past had been made too big for the puny power of their engines. He had built the smallest possible dirigible. His twelve horsepower engine would be just sufficient to push his dirigible, which, deflated, was tiny enough to be packed into a valise. A few friends gathered to watch the foolhardy enterprise. His dirigible rose, drifted over the trees, bucked the wind, made a turn. Elated, Santos shifted his sand bag to get the dirigible to dip and rise; then flew it up 1,300 feet. Controlled flight at last!

To get down to the ground, he pulled open the top valve to release some of the hydrogen. He emptied too much gas. To make matters worse, the air ballonet inside the large gas bag had sprung a leak and his bicycle pump became useless. Halfway down, his cigar-shaped bag doubled up like a jackknife. The ship began falling more rapidly and was heading for a fatal crash on a football field where boys were playing. With amazing presence of mind, Santos shouted to them to grab the guide ropes which were already trailing along the ground and to run against the wind. The boys followed his instructions quickly. The bag righted itself and softened the crash landing, miraculously saving the life of the pilot.

Santos was delirious with joy. It was the first time in history that a balloonist had maneuvered in every direction, up and down, left and right, and in a circle.

No one was more excited than Henri Deutsch, a wealthy entrepreneur, who had stated back in 1889 that "in the petrol engine lies the solution to the problem of aerial navigation." He saw the first fulfillment of his prophecy in the flight of Santos. Forthwith, he began to organize the Aero Club of France to encourage further experiments. A 100,000 franc prize was offered by Deutsch to the first person who could fly to the Eiffel Tower and back within thirty minutes from a distance seven miles away in a lighter-than-air craft. Comte Albert de Dion was delighted that his engine had made the first successful flight in the air. He donated land at St. Cloud to be used for aviation. Santos built a hangar and workshop there, provided with outlets of hydrogen and coal gas, to fabricate his future dirigibles.

As he built his dirigibles (fourteen in all), Santos learned how to improve them, risking his life over and over again. His second dirigible landed him on a tree on a private estate. Reporters, rushing to the scene, found him sitting on a limb nonchalantly drinking a bottle of beer graciously provided by the Countess on whose estate he had landed. The guide rope of his third became tangled in telegraph wires and ripped his bag. He found himself sitting on a ledge of the Hotel Trocadero, as his gas bag burned, waiting to be rescued by a fire department ladder.

The near escapes of Santos Dumont took Paris by storm. The city had not experienced such a lift of spirit since the days of Nadar and the first balloon of Charles. A gaping populace saw their hero dancing on the catwalk of his dirigible playfully keeping it level. Taxicab drivers, on seeing him flying over the rooftops of Paris, would wave their leather caps and shout "Vive Santos." There was no one like "le petit Santos." One moment he was a dandy, elegant with buttoned boots, high starched collar, light colored gloves and glossy top hat. And the next moment, he was a daredevil dancing a tango over the rooftops of Paris.

He became the living embodiment of a Jules Verne hero, surviving near disasters with cool, quick resourcefulness. His fortune could have provided him with the whole gamut of pleasures, but he preferred to risk his life as a daredevil pioneer. "Le petit Santos" became more than a daring Verne hero. Paris took him to its heart as a simple, honest human being.

Santos began to compete for the 100,000 franc prize offered by Deutsch with his fourth dirigible. His sixth dirigible had circled the tower, when the engine stopped. Santos crawled along the keel with a pair of pliers. He succeeded in restarting the engine, but he lost several minutes. He raced the dirigible back to the starting point within the thirty minutes, but he was still in the air, and it took him another thirty seconds to descend. This time, the entire French press demanded that the judges give him the prize, which they did. The prize money went to the poor, endearing Santos to the populace all the more.

Santos' search for a tiny blimp as an aerial taxi for his pleasure and personal use had started a new aeronautic wave circling the world. Balloons began to perform spectacular stunts. One crossed the Mediterranean Sea. Even Nadar's dream was fulfilled by the long-distance voyage of Count Henri de la Veaux, who flew 1193 miles from France to Russia in 35 hours and 45 minutes.

In the five short years after Santos first flew, the building of dirigibles became international in scope. The belief became universal that lighter-than-aircraft would capture the world market for both passengers and freight.

The Lebaudy brothers sprang a surprise in 1903 with a semi-rigid airship that placed the gondola on the underside of the envelope uniting the two into one structure, and making the first long, sustained flight with 35 horsepower gasoline engines. They were planning to build more rigidly framed airships, big enough to carry several engines and to transport passengers and mail from city to city.

In Germany, Count Ferdinand von Zeppelin took up the challenge of future air transport with an airship, made rigid with aluminum trusswork, completely covered inside and out with specially treated linen and silk. Its seventeen ballonets contained 350,000 cubic feet of hydrogen, capable of lifting a ten-ton craft. A rudder controlled the lateral movement, while a sliding weight, similar to one Santos used, managed the dipping and soaring. When the secret airship was pulled out of its hangar, spectators were staggered by its size, but it soon became evident that its two sixteen horsepower Daimler benzine engines, slung beneath in two aluminum cars, were inadequate. It managed to fly for only twenty minutes at eight miles an hour.

There was one other competitive threat to Santos' becoming the first to conquer the air with controlled flight. He had heard the disturbing lecture of Octave Chanute at the Aero Club. Chanute had predicted that the glider would soon be converted into an airplane. He revealed the secret of lateral stability and persuaded some members to begin work on the kind of biplane glider originated by the Wright brothers

In 1905 Santos had heard that the Wright brothers were making long, sustained flights at a field some eight miles from Dayton, where farmers and trolley passengers swore that they had seen a flying airplane. His friends dismissed it as a yarn, but Santos assumed it might be true, and he began studying the principles of the glider.

It was enough for others to say it couldn't be done to stir Santos to prove the contrary. He remembered a game he had played as a child, called "flying birds." The children, seated around a circle, had to raise a finger if the interlocutor made a statement that was incorrect. "A chicken can fly; a pigeon can fly; a man can fly." Santos didn't raise his finger. He stubbornly refused to pay a forfeit for the statement considered to be incorrect. He insisted that men would fly—some day. In this spirit, he wrote an article in 1905 about the future of manned flight. Santos visualized giant balloons that would fill the skies, carrying the world's passengers and freight traffic.

The air age, Santos wrote, had just been launched. The competition between lighter and heavier-than-air craft would grow increasingly keener, as Jules Verne had predicted. At this point in his article, Santos promised his readers a stupendous surprise. "What would you say," he addressed his readers, "if I told you that I hope in the Summer of this year . . . to be able to cruise over Europe for a whole week, in an aerial yacht?"

Santos, in fact, had been secretly experimenting with Hargraves' box kites, hoping to combine them with his dirigible.

In this way, he hoped to be able to hover over a city at night with his gas bag and speed away on the box kites by day at fifty miles an hour.

The future world, Santos rhapsodized, would march on to the synchronized roar of aero engines. Each city would have its airport just as it had its railroad station. "They will have waiting rooms, restaurants, bars, car parks adjoining and will include belts for the conveying of machinery and gas producers."

Santos' dream of bringing in the golden age of the dirigible himself was dashed when in June of 1905 the Lebaudy brothers demonstrated their new passenger dirigible, making a flight that lasted three hours and eleven minutes at thirty miles an hour. It was the first airship to be fitted with both horizontal and vertical fins at the tail and to carry many passengers. The dirigible seemed complete to Santos. There was nothing for him to do. So he decided to concentrate on building the first practical heavier-than-air machine.

By this time many members of the Aero Club had embarked on projects to make an airplane. Ernest Archdeacon, the new President of the club, had built a Wright glider as Chanute had described it in his lectures. Gabriel Voisin flew it, not too successfully, from the sand hills at Berck. Bleriot had been experimenting with Hargraves' box kites since 1901 and had already gone through a dozen crashes. The Farman brothers and a half dozen other aeronauts were also deep in such experiments, when Santos decided to hire Voisin to help him build a powered glider.

The wings, the fuselage, the tail assembly, the engine and the propellers of Santos' plane were arranged and rearranged like drawings on a study board. Archdeacon offered a prize to the first airplane simply to lift itself into the air. But the problems seemed insurmountable. How to get the mathematics of power-weight ratio, camber, stability, control, center of gravity and lift to form a balanced equation? Voisin gave up, but Santos, with his usual stubbornness, persisted in tackling the most challenging problem of his life.

Little by little the mathematical equation began to have a more perfect balance. The main structure became a series of boxes made of wire struts, paneled with fabric, lavishly braced with piano wire. Santos realized the importance of having a pronounced dihedral angle between the main planes for lateral stability. The engine was placed between the wings with the propeller behind and the fuselage extended forward, ending in a small box-kite cell, which could be swiveled left and right and up and down.

As an extra precaution, to keep the plane stable, Santos devised two surfaces, octagonal in shape, mounted between the outer wing struts. Wires led from them to a metal T-piece sewn into the back of a special coat. Santos decided to wear such a coat standing up so that he could sway his airplane one way or another by hip movements. Like the Wright brothers, he had found a way to change the shape of the plane while in the air.

He aptly named his first machine *The Infuriated Grasshopper*. It was a weird specimen. It looked as if boxes had been piled around a central box cell, like so many afterthoughts, added helter-skelter at the spur of the moment. But he had checked his mathematics over and over again, and they proved he could control the flow of air to give him the necessary lift.

Everything now depended on the engine. As a child, Santos' father had taken him to the Great Exhibition in Paris. Santos had never forgotten the gleaming model of an internal combustion engine. It was a one horsepower single cylinder engine of polished steel and brass, clacking away like an imprisoned demon. He had been mesmerized, as if Fate had ordained him to focus his mind on mechanics. And now Fate brought him to the recently completed, twenty-four horsepower Antoinette engine to lift his aerodynamic glider into the air. Santos had made his plane as light as possible so that it might be lifted, not by a catapult, but by the wind storm created by the propeller itself.

A large crowd assembled on October 23, 1906, to witness the historic demonstration. The propeller was whirled and began clacking, gathering speed as it moved across the field. Suddenly, the wheels lost contact with the earth. Then the fragile apparatus of bamboo and cloth fell hard on the earth and cracked up.

But there was a roar of acclamation from the crowd. They had seen it fly. The judges, using a tape measure, discovered that Santos had flown thirty-six feet in a straight line, at twenty-three miles per hour, at a height of ten feet. Their

The Santos-Dumont biplane. *Smithsonian Institution.*

decision came in a written statement: "It is the first time that a motor driven airplane has taken off on its own power and flown."

On November 12th, 1906, after *The Infuriated Grasshopper* was repaired, and a second trial made, members of the Aero Club clocked Santos as moving through the air for 720 feet in 21.5 seconds, at a height of about 20 feet.

For the man in the street this was the world's first public and successful flight of a powered machine. It marked the true beginning of the age of aviation. Although the Wright *Flyer* had covered about twenty-five miles two years earlier, it was a phantom biplane, and the bicycle mechanics who flew it were shadowy figures without a real image.

In contrast, the Paris editor of *The New York Herald* called the Santos hop "the first mechanical flight of man." The headline of a London paper blazoned: "The First Flight of a Machine heavier-than-air!" Santos won the French Aero Club prize for the first public airplane flight in Europe by covering twenty-five meters. The Legion of Honor was conferred upon him. And then came the most precious honor of all—the scientific wizard of the age sent him a note: "To Santos Dumont, the pioneer of the air—homage from Edison." Santos was the hero of the hour, the man who had conquered the air with both a lighter- and a heavier-than-air craft.

Launching the Air Age

THE SENSATION OF THE SANTOS DUMONT FLIGHT WAS TO PROVE a blessing in disguise for the Wright brothers. No one dared speak now of engineering impossibilities. Captain Ferber pleaded fervently with the American aeronauts to come to France quickly to negotiate a contract. The time never had been so ripe and the Wrights were galvanized into action. They crated their plane, stored it in Le Havre, and arrived in Paris in the late summer of 1907 to discuss terms.

While negotiations were going on, Captain Ferber introduced the Wrights to the distinguished members of the Aero Club. Deutsch and Archdeacon were offering a 50,000 franc prize award for the first airplane to fly one kilometer in a closed circuit. The Santos Dumont flight had been a flop, and the French hero had abandoned box kites to work on a tiny biplane that he might use as a personal taxi instead of a dirigible. The Wrights saw a powered box kite Voisin had created stagger like a drunken dragonfly.

The brothers were astonished to find that no aviator seemed to understand the wing-warping technique for lateral stability. A member of the Aero Club, R. E. Peletier, claimed that he had copied a Wright biplane as Chanute had described it, but had found it impossible to fly. The Aero Club had been persuaded that lateral stability was not as important as Chanute had claimed.

The French company negotiating with the Wrights pleaded for a demonstration flight before offering a price. They could not believe that the Wright *Flyer* was more advanced than the box kite planes of Voisin and Santos Dumont. Wilbur sized up the situation and concluded that the French had nothing. No one had yet tried to win the 50,000 franc offer for a circular flight, which they had already performed in 1904.

The prize money was laughable to Wilbur. He was demanding a down payment of a quarter-million dollars that would be cancelled if he were not able to fulfill all requirements. Once again, negotiations broke down. The brothers returned home, but they left the crated plane in Le Havre. Wilbur sensed that he was in a strong position. Sooner or later, the French would have to agree to his terms, which were fair and would protect him from any possible fraud.

The old Chinese proverb "nothing is so full of victory as patience" became a truth for the Wrights. They had written and published a long article in *Century Magazine*, explaining in detail how they had built their *Flyer*, circled a mile, and flown non-stop for 25 miles in 1905. The article stirred President Theodore Roosevelt to order an investigation by the War Department. In February, 1908, the U.S. Army at last wrote to the Wrights offering them $25,000 for an aeroplane that met specifications. The letter was a signed contract.

The specifications were formidable. The plane should be able to carry two persons with a combined weight of no more than 350 pounds. There should be enough fuel to cover 125 miles at 40 miles per hour. The pilot should be able to steer in all directions without difficulty, "at all times under perfect control and equilibrium." The plane should be easily and quickly taken apart, and reassembled in one hour. The Wrights knew they were the only ones in the world who could meet all these requirements.

The following month, a signed contract arrived from the French company with more modest specifications. The plane should be able to fly at least thirty-one miles with a passenger even through a twenty-five mile-an-hour wind. The brothers would receive $100,000 and fifty percent of all profits. Orville agreed to pilot one plane for the United States Army in Virginia, while Wilbur would demonstrate a twin plane in Le Mans, 130 miles west of Paris.

They gave themselves a week's practice in Kitty Hawk before they went their separate ways. Late in May Wilbur shipped his crated machine from Le Havre to Le Mans. Upon arriving in Le Mans, he learned that his *Century* article had created an angry furor in France. The French press was infuriated by his preposterous-sounding claims. A sneering press item mentioned "a Monsieur Wilbug Bright," who imagined himself the original inventor of the airplane. *The Paris Herald* minced no words: "The Wrights have flown or they have not flown. They possess a machine or do they possess one? They are, in fact, either flyers or liars."

To make matters worse for poor Wilbur, his crated machine arrived in Le Mans badly damaged and dented in many parts. Bolts and nuts were scattered and missing. It seemed a deliberate provocation. Wilbur had to spend precious months replacing damaged and missing parts by having them rebuilt again in the automobile plant of his friend, Leon Bolle. Fortunately, he had until the end of October to fulfill the demands of the contract.

By midsummer the members of the Aero Club had all arrived in Le Mans to test their latest designs. Wilbur saw Bleriot crashing another monoplane. He wondered how Henri Farman could have circled a mile with his staggering box kite plane earlier that year. He heard that Santos Dumont had failed to complete his tiny, new plane.

News arrived from the United States that Glenn H. Curtiss had won the *Scientific American* award for circling a mile before a great crowd in New York. Another American had won universal acclaim while the Wright brothers were still under a cloud of misunderstanding. Wilbur could afford to wait no longer. He announced that he would make the first test flight on August 8th, at a local racetrack five miles south of Le Mans.

Since he could not fly his plane directly off the ground, he had to set up a heavy weight-and-derrick rig to catapult the *Flyer*. By this time so much curiosity had been aroused by the American "bluffeur," who pretended he knew how to fly, that several reporters arrived from Paris to join in the fun.

On the day of the trial he wore a simple business suit and a high starched collar, but his green shirt and golf cap gave him the appearance of a "hick". When questioned by reporters, he answered "My contract states that I must fly, not hop from the ground, or flutter along like a hen chased by a dog." It was a boast as well as a rebuke to the French aeronauts, who had made such a poor showing at the trials.

The members of the Aero Club were only too willing to have Wilbur make good on his boast. Though dressed in their Sunday best, they helped drag the long, heavy rope to pull the great weight up to the top of the derrick. The engines were started and Wilbur took his pilot's seat, tightened his jaw and pulled the catapult release. The wheeled car supporting the *Flyer* rolled rapidly along the track. Wilbur raised the nose of his plane; the restraining rope slipped off and the plane rose thirty feet into the air.

What followed happened with the swiftness of lightning. The spectators watched the performance in utter disbelief. With complete ease and aplomb, Wilbur circled his plane twice within a radius of not more than seventy yards, turning at the terrifying angle of thirty degrees. He made two effortless circuits, including a tight figure eight over the grandstand, before touching down, lightly and softly, on the iron skids of the plane. The 107-second flight astounded the French aeronauts. They had never expected to witness an airplane maneuver as smoothly as a bird. For the first time they saw no lurching machine intent on tumbling the pilot. Bleriot could only exclaim, "It is marvelous!"

The small triumph grew in magnitude the following weeks. The French Army gladly gave permission for the American to use its military grounds at Camp d'Auvours, eight miles outside Le Mans. Word of mouth brought increasing numbers of spectators, eager to see the first real demonstrations of man's mastery of the air. Day after day, Wilbur kept prolonging his flights, as newspapermen and photographers arrived from all over the world to witness the new phenomenon. When Wilbur stayed aloft for 19 minutes, 48 seconds, traveling a distance of 16.5 miles, the crowd was filled with enthusiasm and mobbed the new hero. Reporters described people unashamed of their tears. Cinema houses in Paris showed authentic films of the record-breaking flight and were sold out.

Leading French aviators showed no twinge of jealousy as they cried out in rapture, "We are all beaten . . . Aviation has just begun . . . It was the most exciting spectacle ever presented in the history of applied science." To their honor the French press apologized humbly and profusely. *Le Figaro* stated, "It was not merely a success, but a triumph . . . a conclusive trial and a decisive victory for aviation, the news of which will revolutionize scientific circles throughout the world."

The Aero Club honored Wilbur with a gold medal. Lord Northcliffe offered him $10,000 to cross the English Channel. Wilbur postponed the Channel flight until the late fall, but even then negotiations with French, Italian and German firms prevented him from taking time out for the flight.

A penniless young aeronaut from England made a special bicycle trip from England to shake the hand of the pioneer airman, whom he had championed the year before in a letter to the *London Times*. Wilbur took time out to reveal some of the secrets of his flying machine to the young enthusiast, who had believed the plane existed when no one else did. This time, it was Wilbur's turn to hear A. V. Roe claim that he had made the first unofficial flight in England. The young man returned home to become one of England's giant producers of airplanes.

Altogether, Wilbur had made 104 flights by the end of 1908. On the last day of the year he flew through a drizzle of rain for two hours, 20 minutes and 23 seconds, covering 77 miles, and winning about $7,000 in prizes. He had set world records for distance, altitude and time.

The news from Orville was the one disturbing note in those sweet days of triumph. After making several successful demonstrations of his plane for the U.S. Army at Fort Myers, Orville met with an accident. When he took Lieutenant Thomas E. Selfridge with him for a flight, a new propeller proved to be defective. A split caused a vibration that twisted it, snapping a wire that held the rudder. The plane tumbled from a height of 125 feet. The Lieutenant was killed, and Orville survived with compound fractures of his left leg, thigh and ribs. When he was able to use crutches, he joined his brother in France.

Riches arrived with fame in generous measure for the two brothers, who had endured neglect and suspicion for five long years. Entrepreneurs pleaded for exclusive rights to build the Wright biplane. Italy offered 500,000 francs and twenty-five percent of the profits. Russia presented a check for $100,000 to build ten *Flyers* and agreed to pay $2,500 royalties for each additional machine. The U.S. Army paid $30,000 for the first plane and contracted for four more at $7,500 each.

The First military aircraft in the United States, demonstrated at Fort Meyer, Virginia, September 3, 1908. *National Aeronautics and Space Administration.*

There was money enough now to incorporate the American Wright Company and set up winter quarters in Pau, a resort town in the South of France. Katherine Wright, sister of Orville and Wilbur, who had sewn the linen for all the gliders, gave up her job as a teacher to become the secretary and general manager of her brothers' company.

The sunny days in Pau were the most blissful of their lives for the two brothers. They trained pilots to fulfill contracts. Wilbur became the star attraction for vacationing statesmen and kings. Alphonso of Spain was photographed sitting in a plane, though he was not given permission to fly. The Crown Prince of England, however, disobeyed his father and flew as the first royal passenger. The brothers made a triumphal tour through Europe. Wherever they went, governments prepared medals and honors for them. They were even decorated

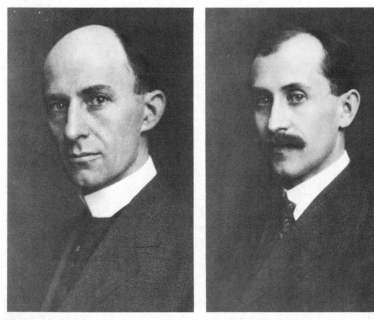

Wilbur Wright   Orville Wright

by a society for universal peace, though their planes had been bought for purposes of war.

Wilbur's dreams of fabulous riches, however, vanished into a mist. He was forced to use the profits he earned in Europe for long and costly legal actions. Competitors who refused to pay royalties sprang up everywhere. By 1912 Glenn Curtiss had become the busiest airplane builder in the United States. That year Wilbur's sense of glory faded in strain, sorrow and a growing mood of pessimism. He contracted typhus and died. Bishop Wright wrote this epitaph for his son: "A short life full of consequences. An unfailing intellect, imperturbable temper, great self-reliance and as great modesty; seeing the right clearly, pursuing it steadily, he lived and he died."

Orville never truly recovered from the death of his brother. In 1914 the United States Court of Appeals, Second Circuit, recognized the Wright brothers as "pioneers in the practical art of flying with heavier than air machines." Curtiss was pronounced an infringer on their patents. The powerful financial group behind Curtiss continued the legal battle even to the point of having Curtiss test the original Langley machine at Hammondsport, New York. After adding thirty improvements, he succeeded in getting it to fly in short hops, thus gaining a legal point.

Weary of the prolonged legal battle that had already cost him $250,000, Orville decided to sell out in 1916 to a financial group of automobile men. Thus Orville missed by one year, a billion dollar order of planes for World War I.

The entry of the United States into the war came as a complete shock to Orville. He had believed all along that his invention would make further wars too frightful, and that statesmen would find other ways of settling their disputes. He lived to see air power extended to the mass bombing of cities in two world wars. Before the end of his life he expressed regret that he and his brother had ever invented the airplane.

Glen Curtis on one of his early planes.
Smithsonian Institution.

Another early Curtis plane. *Smithsonian Institution.*

It was Wilbur's demonstrations in France and Italy that actually launched the air age in 1908. For the first time, the French aeronauts grasped the importance of lateral stability. Henri Farman abandoned his box-kite plane to build one that followed Wright's design and flew a distance of eight miles. Wing warping gave Bleriot the stability to fly his monoplanes, and Delagrange flew for half an hour. More than a hundred engine makers worked feverishly to create more power. They discovered new systems of cooling and fuel injection to raise engine capacity to fifty horsepower.

It was as if the Wrights had opened a magic door. The following year, 1909, an air madness swept the world with thirty-six balloons, sixty-eight dirigibles, and seventy-six airplanes all in the air. Every week brought news of new advances. The Antoinette monoplane survived a wind of gale proportions. Bleriot created a world sensation by flying across the English Channel in thirty-seven minutes. His twelfth monoplane won him a contract, and he began building 10,000 monoplanes. Santos completed a gossamer design of bamboo and silk that he named *Demoiselle*. Wishing to spread the pleasure of flying to as many as possible, the sportsman-aeronaut presented the design of his plane as a free gift to the world.

1909 was a year of aeronautic headlines. The Santos dream of flying from city to city was made real by Maurice Farman, who flew from Chartres to Orleans, a distance of 43.5 miles, in exactly one hour. Moore-Brabazon of England succeeded in flying a circular mile with a new sixty horsepower Gustavus Green engine. Half of Germany witnessed the Zeppelin navigating up and down the Rhine for twenty-four hours. Russia joined the upsurge when Igor Sikorsky lifted the first four-passenger multi-engined plane. To celebrate the conquest of the air, an international air meet was scheduled in Rheims for August. Two hundred and fifty thousand spectators stormed in to see thirty-eight planes break all previous records.

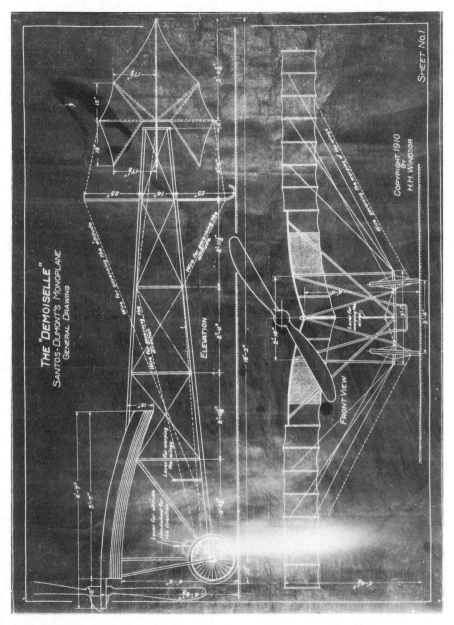

Drawings for the *Demoiselle*, the Santos-Dumont monoplane.
Smithsonian Institution.

It was a year when aeronautic heroes popped up everywhere. S. F. Cody was a typical example. He was a Texan who went to England with a Wild West show, and stayed on to build man-lifting kites for the Navy; one of them set a record by carrying a man up to a height of 3,000 feet. He transformed his kites to powered biplanes, built England's first dirigible and when it was destroyed in a wind storm, rebuilt the wreckage into a giant plane, which he called the *Flying Cathedral.*

The following year there were races from London to Manchester and non-stop flights from London to Paris. When air-mail service began on September 8, 1911, the airplane became part of the workaday world of modern times.

From Dream to Nightmare

THE BUBBLES OF SCIENCE-FICTION ADDED TO THE EFFERVES-
cence over the flying machine and the rigid airship. Rudyard
Kipling, Jules Verne and H.G. Wells peered into the future
during the early years of the twentieth century and prophesied what the future would bring.

Kipling foresaw man molding himself to the demands and
the rhythms of the machine. Kipling's 1910 story, *With the
Night Mail*, visualized the flying machine of 2,000 A.D. It
was a technological wonder, capable of riding out a storm in
a routine mail flight across the Atlantic. A phenomenal
engine swept the 232-foot *Cyclone* through an air maelstrom.
It was "belched up by thermals, spun down by vertices,
clubbed aside by laterals." The powers of the air buffeted it
"like the pinions of angry angels." But the jointless, metal-
plated monster, as sleek as a bullet, shot up through the storm
winds into the serenity of the upper atmosphere.

Kipling leaves us with the uncanny impression that he had
somehow described the air and space vehicle of today, even
though his technology is necessarily vague. The *Cyclone*
maintained its equilibrium in the unstable air by means of a

balancing rudder that projected at the edge of the wings. Radium salts started the heating and circulation of the hot gases. They whirled through the spiral of blades like steam through a turbine engine, "with a force that would whip the teeth of a power saw." At this point Kipling made a startling forecast of the fuel cell that powered the *Gemini* spacecraft by describing the cycling of the gases into liquid and then back into gases again, renewing the energy and preserving the fuel.

For the aeronaut, it was a dazzling glimpse of goals to be attained, a forecast of infinite progress for his beloved mechanical child—the aeroplane.

In Verne's first book on the airplane, published in 1886, the hero, Robur, announced at the end of the book that he would reveal the secret of the airplane only when men would cease to be wolves. Fifteen years later Verne sensed the aggressive madness that was creeping over the world. Armaments were outgrowing all else. Science had made war more potentially destructive than ever.

Verne came to believe that scientists who invented secret weapons were monomaniacs who would die by the new mechanical forces they had released. In *City of the Sahara* scientists were caught in the machinations of a power-hungry adventurer. They worked under contract to build a mechanized city in the Sahara. After they were paid off, they used the airplanes they had invented to take them back to their homes, unaware of the assassins hired by the dictator to extinguish their lives and rob them of the money they had so faithfully earned.

The last stories of Verne were meant to be warnings disguised as thrillers. But the warnings were lost on his readers because Verne made outlaw inventors the arch enemies of society, demented individuals who were prepared for ruin and death if they could not rule.

H.G. Wells in his *War in the Air*, published in 1908,

gave his readers more of a jolt. Thousands of flying machines and airships took to the sky like flies roused from filth, to make the entire earth a slaughterhouse of disease and death. Innocents were slain by the mechanical birds of ill omen. Wells also disguised his sermon as a thriller, but he spelled out the reasons why he believed war in the air was inevitable.

The idea for writing *War in the Air* came to Wells when he saw the British Army Dirigible No. 1 flying over London in October, 1907. As the airship proved that it could circle St. Paul's, everyone talked of the coming age of air travel. Wells, on the contrary, had a horrifying vision of the wanton destruction of great cities from the air. In the second Hague Conference of 1907, only 27 out of 44 powers agreed to the non-combatant use of the airplane. For Wells it was an ominous sign. He saw German squadrons of airships, constructed in secret, gaining mastery of the air, sinking battleships in minutes, and attempting the conquest of nations by surprise attacks.

The six great powers of the Earth were arming themselves like children collecting toy soldiers, each trying to get ahead of the others. Only a spark was needed to start a war. The nation that had the decisive weapon would be tempted to use it.

Secret weapons had won wars in the past. Alexander had conquered the world by building light catapults on wheels and using them as field artillery. Napoleon had met his Waterloo when Lieutenant Shrapnel's shells exploded and scattered death over the heads of the charging French cavalry. All the advanced nations were buying Hiram Maxim's rapid-fire gun because it could fire ten bullets a second. These machine guns could be transported through the air a thousand times faster than they could be dragged over the ground.

Wells begins his 1907 tale on a perplexing note: "Everybody talked of flying, everybody repeated over and over again 'Bound to come' . . . There were these Wright Brothers out in America. They glided. They glided miles and miles. Finally, they glided off stage. Why, it must have been nineteen hundred and four, or five, they vanished."

There was something mysterious about machines that flew and then were not heard of again. Wells pointed to the reason. It was the War Office. The nations were developing air programs in secret. Wells had his young Cockney hero take off in a runaway balloon that carried him, accidentally, into the very heart of Germany's impressive air armada poised to embark for a surprise attack on the United States. The balloonist was mistaken for the inventor of the aeroplane who had defected to sell his secret to the German War Office. He was ushered into the presence of a Nordic superman with a Viking helmet, and was received as an honored guest.

The adventures of the Cockney hero followed the usual hairbreadth escapes of thrillers. What was more important was Wells' prognostication of the future, which, on the whole, was a truthful analysis, all the more remarkable for having been made before the world knew a truly practical airplane or airship.

The Germans left in the dead of night for a surprise attack from the air. The United States had to be struck first because it was developing flying machines out of Wright's model. It had to be hit before their plans developed too far. The German air flotilla released parasite airplanes that destroyed the American fleet in a matter of five minutes. The United States capitulated before the terrible threat from the sky. The Germans took possession of the city of New York. But this was only the beginning.

The most impressive forecast in Wells' analysis was his description of the escalation of wars. There was no such thing as a knock-out punch. A large city like New York was not easily subdued. Guerrilla warfare broke out. An appalling massacre of the population followed. Zeppelins rained down bombs that reduced the city to rubble. But revolt spread to other cities, where the United States was able to build a fleet of airplanes that began attacking the airships.

Wells was saying that wars, once started, could not be controlled. France and England, fulfilling treaty obligations, attacked Germany. Every country had been hiding flying machines, bristling with guns. The air fleets of the world dropped death everywhere. Aerial warfare spread from nation to nation without achieving clearcut victory for either side. Aggressors and victims alike were in the clutch of disaster. Each nation devoted all its energies to building planes by the thousands and to training aeronauts by the hundreds of thousands. War became, perforce, a universal guerrilla war, inextricably involving civilians, as city after city was bombridden into rubble. Like the escalation of war, there was an escalation of destruction until civilization, itself, became a shambles.

It is not too late for Wells to have predicted truly. We still have not reached the point where we can say that such universal destruction will never be.

The Mechanical Phoenix

As H.G. WELLS PREDICTED, IT WAS THE RIGID AIRSHIP THAT made the more spectacular showing, when the dream of flight burst into reality. In the early part of the twentieth century, Count Zeppelin created the aircraft, after a half a dozen failures, that seemed the most likely passenger vehicle. The design of his first airship, in 1900, was very like one created by George Cayley back in 1840. An aluminum framework kept a series of inner bags in shape, and because of the weight of the aluminum the Zeppelin had to be made as gigantic as Cayley had visualized it. Instead of Cayley's steam engine, Zeppelin used two Daimler marine motors that had the horse-power of a modern motorcycle, which proved insufficient to push a 400-foot airship against a stiff wind. The producer had to scrap his ship to help pay off his debts.

He was not able to drum up enough money for a second airship until five years later. New features were then added. The engines delivered 170 horsepower, five times as much as the first marine motors. Instead of a sliding weight to glide up and down, there were elevating surfaces operated from the cabin beneath. He gained better control with two wing-shaped stabilizer fins and steering fins, both at stern and bow. He succeeded in traveling for two hours, bucking winds of twenty-five miles per hour. It was an encouraging beginning. The sales of lottery tickets enabled him to build bigger and better Zeppelins.

The fourth ship was propelled by 208 horsepower, which took it to Switzerland and back. On August 4, 1908, it made a twenty-four-hour flight along the Rhine, capturing the imagination and enthusiasm of the people. But back at the starting post, a windstorm swept it against telegraph wires, where a spark set the hydrogen on fire, destroying the airship.

Editorials heaped abuse upon "that crazy old Count" who had nothing but a record of failures. "Never in engineering history has so great an expenditure been made with so little practical results." Count Zeppelin, over seventy, bowed his head in resignation. He had followed a dream that the huge rigid airships could provide mass transportation, and after ten years of effort nothing remained but a charred skeleton.

He woke up the next morning to find a ton of mail, enclosing money. The mail continued to pour in, reaching the huge popular subscription of 6,096,555 marks. This unexpected demonstration of patriotism was a spontaneous command by his countrymen to go on with his work.

Every new ship brought a more efficient design until finally the Daimler-Mercedes engine, housed in a twenty-foot aluminum car, fixed rigidly to the frame, developed 220 horsepower. Each engine drove three-bladed metal propellers of fifteen-foot diameter. The gas departments were divided by sheet aluminum, with pressure gauges to release the excess gas. There were stabilizing and rudder planes in the rear and dipping planes forward and stern.

An air speed of forty-seven miles per hour at last made it practical to take on passengers. Airports were built in the principal cities, and six ships started the first passenger and airmail service. Punctual as railroads, they flew 170,000 miles, carrying 40,000 passengers without a single fatality. By 1914, new designs had attained a speed of seventy miles per hour, and a ceiling of 25,000 feet. The *Dalag* fleet achieved a record of 1,000 take-offs and landings during 3,200 hours of air time before World War I. Plans were being made to expand the service all over Europe and around the earth.

The airplane before World War I underwent the same technical struggles, but made a poorer public showing. When C. P. Rogers started from New York in a Wright plane in 1911, he hoped to win the Hearst $50,000 prize by crossing the country in the allotted thirty days. He crashed so many times that when he reached Los Angeles 89 days later, on crutches, nothing remained of his original plane except a rudder and a strap.

While the Zeppelins were carrying passengers from Germany to Switzerland, the airplane was still a frail thing of wood, wire and fabric, barely able in calm air to carry two men forty miles an hour. The stick and wire biplanes were structurally weak, incorrectly designed, woefully underpowered. The wings barely supported their own weight, so that a pilot could climb only a few feet. He had to level off to pick up lost speed. The flow of air was so slow that ten miles an hour could make the difference between top speed and a nose dive.

Pilots had to fly, as they expressed it, "by the seat of their pants." Even when ailerons took the place of wing warping, the raising of the left wing flap to make a turn would lower the right wing and cause the plane to yaw (skid) to the right. This tendency to yaw in a direction opposite to a turn had to be quickly corrected by swinging the rudder. The pilot had to be constantly vigilant. A sudden push by a gust of wind spelled real danger. Unless the pilot was instantly responsive, the uncontrolled plane would plunge. By 1911

Early U. S. Army plane, with pilots and mechanics.
Smithsonian Institution.

there had been more than a hundred fatal crashes, because
pilots were not quick and skillful enough.

After every flight a plane required a complete rehauling. One
loose nut might mean a broken neck. Pilots were constantly
repairing their flying crates with sewing kit, hammer, and
pliers, which they always kept in their pockets. They fussed
over their canvas and wire biplanes as they might over delin-
quent children. And yet, the aeronauts gloried in the feeling
that their next flight might be their last. They had to be
adventurers as well as mechanics. To plunge into the new
dimensions of space brought more rapture than fear. They
were like airborne cowboys, determined to coax their aerial
wild horses to obey their will. As a matter of fact, the United
States Army placed pilots in the Cavalry Division. Regulations
demanded that Army pilots wear spurs.

The French aeronauts began to demand better planes and more inherent stability. The fifty horsepower engine came in to dispense with the need for rail and derrick take-off. The propeller was placed out in front, to get better control over the tail surfaces. The pilot was enclosed in a canoe-like fuselage to protect him from the wind blast. All control surfaces were placed in the rear, and a wheeled under-carriage took the place of skids.

Engineers became convinced that the biplane produced more drag than was realized. They followed Bleriot in building monoplanes. They experimented with all-metal frames, and internally braced wings. They followed Manly in revolving the engines, like a fan, to save the weight of water cooling. They found it easier to fly by having one stick pushed in different directions to control the different surfaces. The control stick became so simple to operate, it was nicknamed the "joy stick."

The new monoplanes, first in France and then in Germany and England, meant a more rapid rate of climb, reaching a record of 20,000 feet in altitude. It gave airplanes the height they would need to serve as reconnaissance planes in case of war. War departments raised their specifications. They demanded airplanes from engineers that were stable under all conditions of flight, so that pilots need not concern themselves at all times with continuous adjustments of controls.

To get more inherent stability, engineers placed the horizontal stabilizer in the rear, tilting it forward to prevent the nose of the aircraft from pitching. Then they hinged an elevator to the stabilizer to control the angle of attack of the wings by moving the tail up or down. A vertical fin was added to assist in controlling the direction of flight. Attached to the vertical fin was a movable part, the rudder, which was used to control turns in conjunction with the ailerons.

But even this was not enough. The French War Department offered 50,000 francs for an automatically stabilized plane. It was an American inventor who won the prize. A teenager, Lawrence Sperry, believed that his father's gyroscope, used in stabilizing ships, might be adapted to airplanes. The first automatic pilot was installed in a Curtiss plane just before the war.

The key to gyroscopic control is that the right pressure against the top of a moving gyroscope can change its direction. Sperry clustered four gyros within a metal frame. He placed electric brushes around the frame to collect signals from the gyroscopes which resisted pressures. The signals were transmitted to clutches which could make any necessary corrections in the controls.

If the plane were pitching, the elevators automatically took over. If the signal indicated yaw (movement to right or left), the rudder took over. If the plane rolled (movement around the longitudinal or fore-and-aft axis), the ailerons made corrections.

Ten years before Jules Verne had imagined an automatic control to balance his imaginary plane by the movements of a central pylon that acted upon sliding weights. It never occurred to him that a spinning top and electro-magnetic circuits would accomplish the same end. The engineer proved to be more imaginative than the writer of science fiction. Sperry's automatic pilot could stabilize and control the airplane in a straight and level flight better than a human pilot could do. It kept the airplane parallel to the ground, no matter what the attitude (change in directional position) of the plane might be at any given time. On testing the automatic pilot, the French report said, "The airplane, abandoned and apparently thrown out of equilibrium, continues to navigate at the rate of forty to fifty miles an hour."

When World War I broke out, sooner than expected, all over Europe, the Germans followed H.G. Wells and decided to use their Zeppelins to terrorize England into submission.

Both Wells and the authorities proved to be wrong. The fifty-eight bombing raids carried out were a military stupidity. The Zeppelins' huge size, slowness, and clumsiness in maneuvering made them easy targets even for the early fragile planes.

Nevertheless, the Germans persisted in following the fantasy of Wells. Towards the end of the war, they designed a 2.5 million cubic foot Zeppelin, with a range of 10,000 miles and a bomb load of twenty-eight tons, in a daredevil project to bomb New York City. Captain Strasser, the guiding madman of the Zeppelin raids, was shot down over London on August 5, 1918. The plan for the bombardment of New York was dropped.

However, Verne's 1863 fantasy of a transcontinental, steerable balloon was fulfilled during the war. The fifty-ninth Zeppelin built by the Germans amazed the world by flying non-stop to Khartoum and back—4,180 miles in 97 hours. On a mission to help besieged German East Africa, prepared to fly 6,000 miles and back, this Zeppelin received a false report that East Africa had surrendered and turned back, half-way towards its goal. It could be seen, however, that the rigid airship was essentially a ship of peace rather than a menace in war.

The airplane factories were caught unprepared by the war. Production of improved designs had not yet started. France had built 2,000 planes, none of them specially built as combatants. Germany had secretly prepared herself with 1,500 monoplanes, the Taubes, that could climb straight up to 2,000 feet for the purpose of spying. England with its 180 biplanes and the United States with its 55 were not even in the picture. In the first year of the war the available biplanes were used only as scouts to procure photographs, maps and reports on enemy movements.

When enemy planes crossed each other, the young pilots waved to one another in comradely fashion. It was just one big, theatrical show, until a British reconnaissance plane brought back a report to Sir John French that General von Kluck was racing to annihilate the British Army in a crushing flank attack. The British Army withdrew just in time to a stronger position, a move that actually saved Paris from the German Juggernaut. The humble biplane had prevented a crushing Allied defeat.

Orders came to prevent enemy pilots from returning with reports. Hating to kill, the volunteer pilots dangled a brick with a rope, hoping to shatter the whirling propeller of the enemy plane. More stern orders came—use revolvers. The good-natured young pilots, trapped in the inhuman logic of war, had to go through a hardening process. Pilots, finally, were forced to become machine gunners. The airplane, itself, had to be transformed into a piece of maneuverable artillery.

The billboard-sized wings and the seventy-five horsepower engine of the early biplanes were incapable of lifting the extra 152-pound weight of a machine gun, mountings and ammunition. British engineers developed the all-metal Peltrie, pre-war monoplane into the Sopwith fighter. Its 100 horsepower engines gave it a speed of sixty-five miles per hour, and a four-hour non-stop flight. It was able to support a machine gun mounted in a nose of duralumin (the metal used in the framework of the Zeppelin). The slots in the nose of the fighter, vertical and horizontal, allowed a sixty-degree range for the machine gun.

The man behind the machine gun was transformed from patrol pilot to war ace. Plane performances became a life-and-death matter as daredevil aces found themselves flying "suicide planes" and flaming coffins. The aeronaut learned to become a test pilot, straining his aircraft to the utmost through screaming dives, rolls and spins. He had to develop skill in aerobatics, practicing to loop the loop and to maneuver out of a deadly spin. To make matters more grim, no parachutes were provided, even though a flaming dive meant incineration for the pilot. The authorities believed that a parachute might tempt the frightened recruit to bail out over enemy lines to the safety of a prisoner of war camp.

Designers and technicians vied with one another to get airplanes to climb steeply and fly high, to be fast and yet easy to handle, to get heavy bombers to fly long distances. As newer, faster, better planes came off the production lines, plane performance increased dramatically. Toward the end of the war, the fuselage was covered, the tail assembly was completed, under-carriage landing gears made stronger. Air frame efficiency increased speeds up to 150 miles an hour, and engine weight decreased from four pounds for every unit of horsepower to 1.9 pounds.

By that time, air strategy was radically changed. Under the leadership of General Billy Mitchell, 1500 planes of all types wrested control of the air from the Germans in the great St. Mihiel offensive of 1918. The Royal Air Force had twelve different types of planes in the air. The United States was turning out 20,000 planes a year, too late to be used at the war front. The days of the individual dog fights by hero-aces were numbered, replaced by battles between massive formations. The knights of the air became mere cogs in a regimental combat team.

Four years of war had changed aviation beyond all recognition. The pioneer airmen had become managers of factories, capable in each nation of producing 30,000 planes a year. Two-seaters had evolved to such multi-engined bombers as the 250-miles-per-hour Handley-Page with its crew of four, and the Italian Caprini with six men and 500-pound "block-busters." The United States developed the Liberty engine with twelve cylinders that delivered 400 horsepower, opening up vast new possibilities for long-distance flights. By 1918 the 60,000 war planes, the sprawling factories and the 13,574 Liberty engines were ready to launch the new era of air travel.

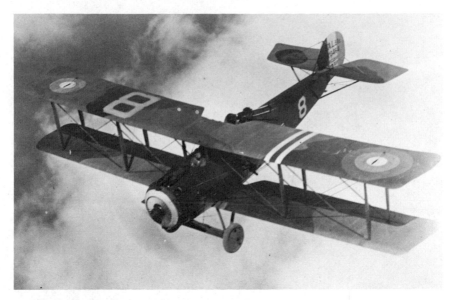

Salmson two-seater observation aircraft—
used during World War I.

Both Official U. S. Air Force Photos.

Spad *13*—Picture taken during Detroit Races in 1922.

Between Two Wars

EAGER TO TEST THE NEW PLANES IN A WORLD AT PEACE, HEROIC pilots in the next two decades made mad dashes across continents, oceans, and the poles of the earth. Four American Curtiss flying boats took off from Newfoundland, and one survived the aerial journey to the Azores, Lisbon and London. The British tried the same flight with their Vickers Vimy bomber. John Alcock and Arthur Whitten Brown described their straight-line dash from Newfoundland to Ireland as "terrible." They flew through fog, rain, snow and sleet practically all the way. Ice formed on the wings; they fell into a tail spin, coming below the clouds to less than one hundred feet above the water. They chopped ice from their instruments. They flew blindly straight ahead until a lucky break in the weather gave them a glimpse of their destination, the wireless station at Clifden. They crashed in a nearby bog with no gas to spare after flying 1,660 miles in 15 hours and 47 minutes.

A month later, England sent its duplicate of a Zeppelin, *R-34*, across the Atlantic. It came cruising over the Mineola airport in Long Island on July 2, 1919, 108 hours after leaving

Scotland. As if to fulfill Poe's dream balloon crossing of 75 hours, the *R-34* made the return trip to England in precisely that time. On May 12, 1926, the Italian airship, *Norge*, piloted by Amundsen with a crew of sixteen, flew over the North Pole and landed in Alaska.

The sense of triumph, however, in fulfilling at last the nineteenth century dream of air conquest, was tainted with the bitter knowledge that the victory was far from complete.

It began to dawn upon engineers that the airplane was still a technological horror, dooming the majority of pilots sooner or later to fatal crashes. The pioneer airmen who were sent off on long-distance flights to open up possible commercial routes had to do so without blind flying instruments, light beacons or radio signals. Three-engined airplanes flew in 300-mile hops from London to Australia in about 27 days, or to Capetown in 45 days, but only after repeated crashes. The triumphs blazed in headlines; the disasters were buried in back pages.

The United States Army Air Service began mail flights as early as May 15, 1918. By 1927, the open cockpit

Loading mail for first night flight to Chicago. Picture taken at Hadley Field, New Jersey. *Smithsonian Institution.*

planes, at best, made 500-mile hops. Crashes were formidable in number. People began to wonder if flying could ever be made safe. The flight over the fog-shrouded Allegheny Mountains was known as the "graveyard run." Of forty pilots who flew it, thirty-one were killed in crashes.

When the airmail service was transferred to private airlines, the companies involved felt the need to fly longer distances. But there was no engine that could fly a plane all the way from Chicago to New York until 1927. In that year airmail pilots began to hear that there was a new 225 horsepower *Wright Whirlwind* engine that had the same weight as the old engines, but was able to deliver more than double the horsepower. The cylinders spun around a hub. Air-cooled, it eliminated the dead weight of radiators and water coolers. It ate up only ten gallons of gasoline an hour and could run non-stop for days at a time.

These facts set off an explosion in the mind of a young mail pilot, Charles Lindbergh. Here was his chance to win the $25,000 prize being offered to the first plane that flew from New York to Paris. There was a newborn engine that could run for two days straight. There existed an all-metal monoplane built by Henry Ford, *The Tin Goose*, that had wings without struts and wires and had proven to be an excellent flying surface, capable of carrying a great load. Strangely enough, it had the dimensions of Sir George Cayley's 1810 sketch of the best possible lifting surface.

At the same time, the Earth Inductor Compass had been unwrapped. This gyroscopic compass could point to the true North and maintain this position unaffected by the metal of the plane. It had none of the weaknesses of the magnetic compass that was constantly deranged by the presence of metal.

Lindbergh had the engine and the precise navigational instrument. All he needed was a plane that could lift 8,000 gallons of gasoline. He learned from engineers that such weight could be lifted for a long-distance flight only if he were to fly alone. The other planes that had entered the transatlantic race had multiple engines and crews of two and three.

There was the possibility that he might not be able to make it alone, but he was willing to take a chance. He communicated his enthusiasm to others. The Wall Street boom of the late 1920's made money available for his project. A special plane, built to his specifications, was made for him in San Diego in a few months' time.

The better wing curvature of the *Spirit of St. Louis* made it possible to carry more fuel at a higher speed for each square foot of wing surface than any other plane. A new chemical mixture of gasoline gave him more miles per gallon. The sturdiness of the aluminized plane was proven in the flight from San Diego to New York. The machine was ready. The rest was up to the skill of the pilot.

Lindbergh decided to fly in weather that was keeping others grounded. He just managed to clear the trees and the telegraph wires at the end of the runway. He had enough experience as a mail pilot not to attempt to fly through the heavy clouds above. Instead he flew around them. As his journey continued, sometimes he preferred to fly under a cloud layer, winging as low as ten feet over the ocean. He did not eat the sandwiches he took along hoping that hunger would keep him awake. Flying at an average speed of 100 miles an hour, he made Le Bourget airport in thirty-three hours.

The pent-up emotions of a century of frustration broke out in frenzied hero worship for one man. He became the symbol of the pioneer who pointed the way to mass air transportation.

The long-distance flight craze that followed kept headlines jumping during the following decade. The reach, unfortunately, exceeded the grasp. The airplane was not technologically perfected for long distances. Of the thirty-one pilots who followed "Lucky Lindy" across the Atlantic, only eleven survived.

But daredevil pioneers kept risking their lives from London to Sydney, from London to Bombay, from Paris to Tokyo. Even the South Pole was attempted, and successfully, by Byrd. All continents were spanned; all oceans crossed. However, the heroes and heroines kept disappearing over Africa, over the Pacific, over deserts, never to be heard from again. When the most daring of them all, Kingsford-Smith, who was the first to cross the Pacific, later vanished over India, the public wanted to hear no more of foolish risks. And the age of thrills was ended.

The air routes had been mapped out. It was time for passenger flight to take over in short hops and with all kinds of safeguards. In 1929 Imperial Airways had begun a weekly service between London and Karachi. By 1933 it was extended to Calcutta, and in 1934 to Australia. KLM flew from London to Batavia; Air France to Santiago, Chile, and to Saigon; Pan American to Cuba and then to the Azores and Spain; Germany from Berlin to Brazil. There were few passengers at first, and the airlines lost money. Governments had to subsidize them. It was risky business to fly, both for passengers and planes, but the service kept on despite all hazards.

The Germans, eight years after the war ended, were permitted to build rigid airships again. They felt that they might be able to capture the passenger market with Zeppelins. After circling the earth and exploring the Arctic, the *LZ-127* began providing scheduled transoceanic air passenger and cargo service. It was the largest object that had ever risen in the sky. Ten miles of girders in a criss-cross maze structure kept its 100-foot-high gas bags rigid; seventy-two miles of fibrous networks surrounded each gas bag to prevent chafing. The gas bags were lined and cemented with thousands of skins from the outside membrane of the large intestine of the ox—

the most gas-impervious material known to man. The ship was so long that anyone standing amidships could see neither bow nor stern. The gas bags were divided into two parts: the upper two-thirds held the hydrogen, the lower part a hydrocarbon gaseous fuel called *Blaugas*, which had about the same weight as air. It powered the five engines below, which were "like five baby whales swimming beneath a mother whale." To compensate for loss of fuel weight, a mechanism "milked" water from clouds that ran down into tanks as ballast.

The 750-feet-long *LZ-127* was among the wonders of the age. On its round-the-world flight eastward from Germany, it pioneered the uncharted wilderness of Siberia. The endless steppeland, as seen by the crew of forty and twenty passengers, was a terrifying panorama of utter wasteland. When the *LZ-127* entered the unexplored Stanovoi Mountains, it had to wind its way through the twists and turns of canyons that kept narrowing and rising dangerously.

At 5,500 feet the hydrogen vented off automatically; precious gas was lost, which might be needed later on. Flying at sixty miles an hour under the guiding genius of Hugo Eckener the Zeppelin just squeezed over the highest ridge, almost scraping the bottom of the hull on the mountain. At last, the ship reached the sunny mirror of the Pacific. Its 102-hour trip across Siberia still ranks as one of the epics of world exploration.

The complete journey, a round-the-world trip in 21 days, 5 hours and 31 minutes, enraptured everybody; it seemed as if Count Zeppelin's dream of global mass transportation was destined to be fulfilled. The Zeppelin provided the most luxurious travel ever known to man. Passengers dined sumptuously at tables with linen and silver, slept in comfortable staterooms, and strolled on a promenade deck for a magnificent view of the ground not far below. There was a complete absence of vibration, motion or noise. The *Graf Zeppelin* completed 634 long-distance trips, flying 1,000,000 miles without an accident, lifting 20,000 passengers through the air with complete satisfaction.

It soon became evident, however, that the giant airships of other nations were still in a state of experimental development. Air turbulence, fire, navigational errors and inexperienced crews destroyed them one after another in epic disasters. The Zeppelin itself had an Achilles heel—inflammable hydrogen. On May 6, 1937, the *Hindenburg*, largest of the Zeppelins, proved that they were not safe after all. According to Dr. Eckener the snapping of a steel bracing wire tore a rent in the fabric of the bag. Static electricity, caused by the swiftly moving hydrogen, burst into flames. The great *Hindenburg* incinerated minutes after it was moored in Lake-

The *Hindenburg* before the disaster that destroyed it.
Smithsonian Institution.

wood, New Jersey, just as the transatlantic passengers were about to disembark.

This disaster doomed all travel by rigid airships, echoing the 1885 prediction of Jules Verne in his *Clipper Ship of the Clouds*. It shocked the Zeppelin engineers, who were blue-printing, at that time, fantastic rotating buildings for airports to minimize delays caused by docking and undocking in cross-hangar winds. They were expecting many new experimental developments in the years ahead. Instead, they came to a full stop.

There are engineers today who believe rigid airships are safe, among them Dr. Morse of M.I.T. He has designed a nuclear-powered 1,000-foot giant of the sky. It would be able to carry a crew of 100 and 400 passengers in staterooms with private baths, a skyroom cocktail lounge to be reached by elevators, a movie theatre and a dining room seating 200. A mid-ship hangar below would hold a helicopter capable of shuttling eighteen passengers at a time to airports of different cities. With its nuclear plant of 6,000 horsepower, it would be able to circle the earth for months at a time.

Modern technology, in fact, can guarantee safety for the next sky giant. A new metal, an alloy of titanium and aluminum, together with new nylon fabric should withstand the stress of the gale force that destroyed the 6.5-million cubic foot *Akron* and the *Macon*. Hydrogen fires that collapsed so many airships will be impossible with helium. The better weather forecasting of today will avoid trips during hurricane conditions. Aerodynamic knowledge will increase speeds to over a hundred miles an hour.

A billion-dollar venture to use nuclear power in airplanes was abandoned because of the weight of the shielding, a weight easily carried by the giant airships. Atomic heating could offer a fuel supply lasting for years. The nuclear airship could inch its way down to almost zero velocity in zero visibility, avoiding in this way the danger of crashing the nuclear reactor. In the future, a two-day leisurely trip from the U.S. to Europe promises to add to the pleasure of vacationers.

Airships would have lost the race against airplanes even without the disasters. In the decade after the Lindbergh boom engineers made daring innovations. The pilots who survived the "graveyard runs" over the Alleghenies, explained the strange effects of "cockpit vertigo." In the midst of clouds the pilots lost all sense of direction. They did not know whether they were going up or down. Thinking they were dashing up out of the clouds, many of them found themselves plunging towards the ground. Blind flying in bad weather proved more dangerous than anyone had suspected it would be.

Engineers licked the problem with gyroscopes and electronics. A young U. S. Air Corps Lieutenant, James Doolittle, made an experimental flight of sixteen miles, flying blindly under the guidance of three instruments.

He steered around the landing field by means of a directional gyro. It was graduated in degress identical to a magnetic compass. When making a turn, the face of the new compass told him how many degrees he was banking or skidding away from the proper circle, or even rolling. An altimeter measured even slight changes in the altitude.

He pulled back slightly on the throttle to descend, keeping his eyes on another revolutionary instrument. On its face was a bar, known as the "artificial horizon," that kept a position exactly like the real horizon, no matter how the plane moved. A miniature airplane outlined on the face of the instrument showed the pilot whether he was headed above or below the horizon.

To land, he followed directions of a third instrument with a small, vibrating reed, whose sound told him whether he was on the best angle to reach the ground. It was oriented to a radio beam transmitted from the airport. Doolittle landed safely, eliminating most of the bugaboos of blind flying.

Every large airplane in the world came to be equipped with these three basic instruments. They made possible the round-the-world flight of Wiley Post in 1931. They added to the safety of the passenger airliner that by this time had circled the world.

Having eliminated the greatest dangers of blind flying, the engineers tackled the threat of stalling speed. It was discovered that at slow speeds the dihedral angle of the wings sometimes threw the air into such turbulence that the plane dropped into a sudden steep dive or else into the slow beginnings of a spin.

F. W. Lanchester, an English aerodynamic genius, had made control of the circulation of air above and below the wings his specialty. There was a desperate need to increase the range of speed a plane could fly from fast to slow. Lanchester's theories revealed that a boundary layer of air next to the skin of the wings was the key air layer to control the sweep of wind. His theory suggested that turbulence could be prevented by a device that smoothed out the onrush of air. Handley Page, a builder of planes in England, solved the problem by using a leading edge slot in front of the wings. The slot absorbed the turbulence, smoothing out the onrushing airflow.

Then it was discovered that the slot increased drag at medium and high speeds. Two-thirds of the power used in a commercial aircraft was used to overcome drag created by turbulence. It was necessary to get the slot to close at higher speeds and open at lower speeds. This was done with a flexible slot, so arranged that the pressure of wind at higher speeds had enough force to push it shut. At slower speeds, it opened up again automatically. Another builder of planes, DeHavilland, tested the slot device for his tiny plane, *The Moth*. He flew it below normal flying speed. He held up the nose of his plane and found himself maintaining lateral controls as *The Moth* slowly sank to the ground.

At last the engineers had learned how to overcome the vicious stall that had killed so many birdmen. Birds, of course, had always used the same idea. They spread individual feathers near the wing tips, creating a kind of lattice arrangement so that airflow can go through easily and not break up in turbulence. The new air control made possible the shorter takeoffs and landings of aircraft.

The engine builders, at the same time, kept increasing the efficiency of power plants. The 225 horsepower of the *Whirlwind* grew to the 425 horsepower of the *Wasp* and to the 900 horsepower of the *Cyclone*. Exhaust valves were improved. By 1935 the air-cooled engines in service were rugged dependable power units. Horsepower could be increased by arranging engines in rows, each row with 3, 5, 7 or 9 cylinders. Rubber pads "floated" the engine in its mounting to decrease vibration. All at once, it seemed, it was possible to carry greater loads and drive at greater speeds. The average speed jumped from 100 miles per hour to 180 miles per hour.

One change could not be made in an airplane, however, without changes in other parts being required. Better engines and better airflow needed better propellers. Different pitch (the distance advanced by a propeller in one revolution) is needed for take off and for cruising. But how could the pitch of the propeller be altered without at the same time changing the number of revolutions per minute of the engine? The variable-pitch propeller was invented to solve this problem. The blades of the propeller could be twisted in their sockets to provide different pitch positions without affecting the speed of the engine.

With all its new capacities for speed and distance, the structure and shape of the airplane itself had to be changed. Dr. B. N. Wallis of England provided a means of constructing a bullet-shaped fuselage. His was a shell-like structure of duralumin, the light-weight aluminum and copper alloy used for Zeppelins. Sheets of the metal were crisscrossed and stressed together into a giant hull. Instead of putting a covering around a structure of wood and wire, as had previously been done, the covering itself became the structure. Wallis created the spindle shape that Cayley, more than a hundred years earlier, had chosen as the form that would offer the least resistance in air flight.

Increased engine power made the full use of metal necessary for the first time. Metal would prove less collapsible in excess stress. It would be more durable, allowing a plane to fly longer distances and climb faster.

The wing became more streamlined. The underside became almost flat. The front half of the wing was thickened but given a sharper leading edge. The rear half was "dished in" toward the trailing edge. The whole thing was given a super-smooth skin with flush rivers. The wing span was decreased. This presented a smaller area against the wind, reducing drag; at the same time, it required less power to pull the same weight through the air. Wind tunnel tests proved that it took only a quarter as much propeller thrust, pound for pound, to pull this airfoil shape through the air than it did to pull along a strut and wire plane. This "laminar flow" wing actually increased lifting power.

The momentum of creativity continued to find improvements. Engineers calculated the right kind of rigid fins and high rudders that would keep a plane balanced, so that it could turn and land even when the engine was shut off. Flaps were added to the wings as brakes for easier grounding on shorter runways.

Boeing was the first airplane builder to make use of all these improvements. The single winged, all-metal, two-engined Boeing 247 of 1933 was the streamlined wonder of the air. To make it even more streamlined, the landing gear was retracted in flight. It reached a speed of 170 miles per hour.

The military fighter was also transformed over night. Since a fighter pilot could never know how high he would have to fly, oxygen masks became part of his equipment. He went so high that a supercharger had to be added to the fighter to compress the thin air at 29,000 feet, thus keeping up the power of the engine so that the propellers could continue to perform effectively. As a final precaution the military pilot was enclosed in a cabin of pressurized air.

Advance in aviation had become so rapid that by 1935 there were 150 aircraft manufacturers, each with a different model plane. The passenger airlines, spreading a network around the earth, began pleading for an air transport that had a 2,500-mile non-stop cruising range at about 150 miles an hour.

In July, 1936, the Douglas DC-3 made its first flight from Chicago to New York. An all-metal monoplane, it had thick wings strong enough to support two of the latest 700 horse power air-cooled engines. It was capable of carrying a useful load of 9,000 pounds, one third more than any preceding plane; of climbing above turbulent weather to a height of 20,000 feet of flying a distance of 2,000 miles at about 200 miles per hour. The thirty passengers were comfortable in their heated, pressurized cabin, with vibration reduced to a minimum.

Douglas had created the miracle passenger plane and scored a major triumph. As the master assembler of scattered engineering advances, Douglas combined in one airplane: single-shell construction; all-metal structure; retractable landing gear; the nesting of the engine within the wing; controllable pitch propellers; wing flaps; supercharger; and cockpit instruments that enabled a pilot to fly through darkness, rain, snow and sleet.

The classic Douglas DC-3 captured the passenger market

The Boeing *247-D*, twin-engine transport of 1934.
The Boeing Co.

The Douglas *DC-3*. *Douglas Aircraft Co., Inc.*

for that period. By 1946, 10,000 had been purchased by 174 airlines in 70 countries. Up to World War II, they carried two million passengers across the Atlantic. Even if the *Hindenburg* had not met disaster, the Douglas air machine would have easily won the race.

Speed

AFTER THE AIRPLANE HAD REACHED A SAFE LEVEL OF INHERENT stability, the constant goal was speed. For the military, who had to deliver their weapons in surprise attacks, speed was all important. So military craft were the pacemakers. More powerful engines and all-metal airplanes made it possible to transfer machine guns to the leading edge of the wings. In 1925, the Curtiss Army Racer reached 247.8 miles per hour. A British Supermarine, specially built for the Schneider Trophy races of 1929, reached 377 miles per hour, developing in time to the famous Spitfires of World War II. By 1934, two Fiat engines of 2,750 horsepower each gave the Italians a record of 440.68 miles per hour. In 1939, the Curtiss Hawk was test-piloted from 22,000 feet into a diving speed of 620 miles per hour. Friction was reduced in the fighter plane by streamlining it into a cigar shape. The Lockheed P-38 climbed a mile a minute and made a transcontinental flight across the United States in less than eight hours.

Bombers made equally formidable progress. Bristling with gun installations in the nose, top, bottom and sides, besides holding 5,000 tons of bombs, the B-17 Flying Fortress could fly for ten hours non-stop, reach a ceiling of 25,000 feet, a speed of 325 miles per hour, and come to a grinding landing with wheel brakes.

When 100-octane gasoline gave an engine dramatic advantages of speed and altitude, more gigantic bombers streamed off the production lines. Boeing's B-29 Super Fortress had a wing span of 141 feet and 31 inches, 20-foot hollow steel propellers and five-foot wheels. Four 2,200 horsepower engines of 18 cylinders each sent it climbing to a ceiling of 30,000 feet and carried a gasoline load that weighed eight times as much as the bombs the plane was to deliver.

These armored battleships of the sky were so sturdy that there is a war record of an inoperable bomber with its gun turret smashed, its wings and rear fuselage pierced with 500 bullet holes managing to reach home base on its belly.

But even the world's largest bomber proved in the end to have a serious limitation. When fighters reached speeds beyond 500 miles per hour, the bomber was not fast enough. Twenty-thousand feet up, the 20-foot propellers lost too much grip on the thinning air. Even after superchargers were added to the engines to compress the thin air to the density of air at ground level, the giant propellers could not push it beyond a top speed of 435 miles per hour. Engineers were baffled when they realized that to double its speed, they would have to give the B-36 twenty-two times more horsepower. It became clear that something new was needed before higher speeds could be achieved.

The air war, prophesied by H. G. Wells in 1908, broke over the world in the late 1930's. Hitler, who had several thousand combat planes, miscalculated the aircraft production capability of his enemies, which reached 300,000 in the United States alone. The American Air Transport Command was an overnight phenomenon that amazed even H.G. Wells. Soon after the war began 3,000 planes were operating fifty-two

The *B-17* over Europe. Part of the stabilizer was blown off but the plane returned to its base.

The *B-29* over Yokohama.

Both photos by The Boeing Co.

daily scheduled flights across the Atlantic and thirty-seven across the Pacific, besides a weekly round-the-world service. Three hundred and fifty global landing fields included such far-out points as a desolate mountain in the South Atlantic, the mid-Sahara desert, coral atolls, icy Greenland and remote Chinese villages over the hump of the Himalayas.

Hitler's hopes for a quick victory by gaining air power over England were stymied when British Spitfire fighters destroyed 1,733 German fighters and bombers. This sent Hitler careening eastward toward Russia on a crazy war for which Germany was unprepared. No wonder it was said of the Spitfire pilots, "Never in the field of human conflict was so much owed by so many to so few."

Allied shipments of 3,000 planes a month to Russia helped bog down the German invasion there. Thousands of allied blimps, seaplanes and planes from aircraft carriers depth-bombed the German submarine menace. Wave upon wave of bombers pulverized the German cities systematically, leaving nothing behind but vast mounds of rubble, ironic monuments to Hitler. The matchstick cities of Japan exploded into flame under a rain of fire bombs from low-flying B-29's, even before the two atomic bombs gave the knock-out punch.

In spite of the devastation wrought by airplanes, their engineers could truly claim a proud record. No machine in the history of civilization had ever made so many advances so quickly. During the war the entire world of technology had concentrated on the flying machine without regard to cost. Metallurgists replaced steel with tungsten to make the more powerful engines heat resistant, extending their life five times. Chemists created new fuels to bring more mileage to a gallon. Mechanical engineers raised engine potential to 3,000 horsepower. Electronic engineers created mechanical nerves that could cope with speeds impossible for human senses.

Mechanical senses began when anti-aircraft gunners on the

ground discovered that they could not hit a target moving as fast as a plane. What they needed was a mechanical man that could respond a million times faster. Engineers already had an electronic tube that pulsed on and off a million times a second. Radar could capture the movement of a plane in a series of blips. The autopilot with its gyroscopes could activate mechanical movements. Firing tables of mathematical calculation could compute at what degree of angle it was necessary to fire a gun at a given time. All this mechanical and electronic know-how was packed into an anti-aircraft battery.

This machine could spot a plane fifteen miles away, figure out its movements, and automatically put a gun into the best position. The human being behind it needed only to press a button in order to fire forty-five shells a minute with deadly accuracy.

Only faster speed could evade anti-aircraft guns, the rain of flak, or long-range radar. The struggle to increase speed brought engineers to reshaping the wings again. The Mustang featured the radical "laminar flow" wing. Its letter S profile helped to smooth out turbulence at high speeds, which slots could no longer handle. The "laminar flow wing" pushed the turbulent air into its hollowed-out section. Drag was reduced by half. Lift was increased, enabling the airplane to fly safer on the same amount of power.

Towards the end of the war the United States had the fastest propeller plane, one that accelerated to just beyond 500 miles per hour. Then the Germans sprang a surprise with an airplane that had no propeller. It took air in the front, mixed it with fuel, and ejected it in the rear in a roaring blast. The jet age had opened up for modern man.

The jet engine was invented by Frank Whittle. As an engineering student he wrote, "It seems that, as the turbine is the most efficient prime mover known, it is possible that it will be developed for aircraft, especially if some means of driving a turbine by petrol can be devised." His professor's margin comment was, "Very original work. Unable to comment." No doubt, the professor was puzzled by the mad idea and wondered what materials could withstand the high temperatures that would be involved.

The turbine engine had been used in airplanes to feed a stream of compressed air into the carburetor to overcome the limitation of rarified air 20,000 feet up. Whittle went one step further. He patented the idea of allowing compressed air to be greatly expanded by heat and then pushed at high velocity out of jet nozzles to create a terrific thrust.

His 1934 patent was not taken seriously by the Royal Air Force until the outbreak of the war. After that, it was a race with time. Germany had begun working on this "new and

The Whittle X-I-X Turbo-jet engine. *Smithsonian Institution.*

secret device" before England. On August 27, 1939, a 16-foot Heinkel was the first jet-propelled aircraft to fly. The Germans made it more efficient when they used broad wings that swept back sharply, increasing the speed to almost 600 miles per hour.

Test pilots were delighted. There was no engine vibration, no lashing sound of a propeller. Jet speed seemed effortless "as though angels were pushing." This was not a step forward. It was an aerial leap. Hitler made one of his greatest mistakes when he stopped experiments on this new fighter in favor of bombers.

The jet engine was fundamentally simple. It had only one tenth as many moving parts as the gasoline engine. It eliminated camshafts, pistons, connecting rods, control mechanisms. It was simply a cone-shaped metal structure that opened at the front end to admit air and tapered to an exhaust jet at the rear. Within the center of the cone was the firing chamber into which the compressed air and fuel was injected under pressure. There were two turbines, one at each end, geared to a single drive shaft. The turbine in the rear was spun by the hot gases. At the same time the turbine at the other end was spinning to compress the air that entered the fuel chamber. It was not the backward thrust of the hot gases against the atmosphere that provided the thrust, as many still imagine, but the pressure at the front end of the exhaust pipe that propelled the aircraft.

While Germany dawdled with jets, England and the United States raced experimentation. First tests were disappointing. A jet plane could remain in the air for only five miles. The fuel consumption of jets was four times faster than that of propeller planes. Then it was learned that the vanes of the gas turbines could not withstand the 1,000-degree Fahrenheit temperatures of the combustion chamber. Near the end of the war a chrome-nickel-steel alloy eliminated this problem, and the way seemed clear to further development.

But by that time, the German jet was in the air, and also the V-2 rocket.

Jet and rocket engines had almost parallel development. There is no difference between jet drive and rocket drive. Both give a forward push to the front end of a tube as the hot gases exit from the rear. But the fact that a rocket engine uses an oxidizer instead of air to burn fuel gives it the unique value of being able to operate outside the earth's atmosphere. In the rocket engine pumps spray the fuel and liquid oxygen into the combustion chamber. The ejection of these burned gases has a more tremendous force than a jet blast.

The principle of the rocket engine was first discovered by Konstantin Tsiolkovsky, "the father of rocketry," back in the 1890's. A Russian high-school teacher of mathematics, he learned in his school laboratory that the power produced by burning kerosene and oxygen gave far more energy than the explosion of guncotton used by Verne to blast his imaginary rocket to the moon. In his exultation Tsiolkovsky broke into tears. He knew he had proved that reaction drive from a tube could ultimately thrust a man up to the moon.

The Russian schoolmaster wrote the theoretical foundation for space flight in mathematical equations and science fiction stories that prophesied man's destiny away from his home planet. An American professor of physics, Robert H. Goddard, transformed the mathematical equations into engineering hardware.

Goddard was granted two patents on rocketry in 1914. He created a combustion chamber with an exhaust nozzle and introduced the flow of liquid oxygen and gasoline into the combustion chamber. To gain higher altitudes, he spelled out the principle of multiple or step rockets. He built this new kind of engine and tested it on March 16, 1926. A small, white flame shot from the exhaust nozzle, and the rocket rose like an elevator and climbed steadily to about 200 feet, then veered

Goddard and his first rocket. *Smithsonian Institution.*

Portion of rocket constructed by Goddard and his
staff in the spring of 1941.
National Aeronautics and Space Administration

and traveled 2,000 feet. A rocket was no longer a glorified
firecracker.

The principles were written out in his classic paper, "A
Method of Reaching Extreme Altitudes." This paper had
more influence in Germany than anywhere else. By April 19,
1932, Goddard had learned how to give his rocket directional
control by putting in a set of gyroscopes. If the rocket veered
from vertical flight, electrical copper brushes, contacting the
brass ring of the gyroscope, would sense any change and
activate a vane to correct the course towards the desired
direction.

He had a more sophisticated set of controls to start the
rocket engine. A button was pressed, a switch was thrown
that started the igniter. A small wire was melted, a weight
was dropped, a valve was opened to release the flow of gasoline. Then levers and weights fell to fire two explosive links

that started the combustion with oxygen and launched the rocket.

The Goddard rocket of 1932 was a miniature in details and components of Germany's *V-2*. Goddard's ideas set Hermann Oberth to writing his book *The Rocket into Interplanetary Space*, which took German youth by storm. A group including Wernher Von Braun organized a society to continue Goddard's experiments. Power-weight ratios began to be studied in rocket engines just as they had been studied for airplanes during the Wright period. The goal was to get thrust to exceed the weight of the fuel.

Johannes Winkler made the first big breakthrough when he lined up two fuel tanks, one behind the other, to give the engine the modern rocket shape. When his rocket shot up to one mile, the German military took over the entire enterprise. On October 3, 1942, a 46-foot missile, weighing fourteen tons, shot up 60 miles, reached a speed of 3,500 miles an hour and landed on a predetermined spot 125 miles from the launching site.

At the same time Goddard himself had been sidetracked to work on bazookas. He had designed the space rocket in the hope of reaching the moon. This studious and gentle inventor never dreamed that his creation would reach the point it has today, when rockets with nuclear warheads can reach any major city of Earth in a matter of minutes.

After the war intensive reasearch went on to increase the size and efficiency of bombers and fighters. The first real jet-propelled combat aircraft, the Lockheed Shooting Star, developed an equivalent of 6,000 horsepower, rose to 35,000 feet altitude and sped across the Atlantic at 550 miles per hour. The Truculent Turtle bomber was able to take on a load of 85,000 pounds, the greatest load in proportion to area of any airplane in history. The B-47 Stratojet with six jet engines increased bomber speed to over 600 miles per hour.

This high speed demanded all kinds of changes from the engineers. Hydraulic power was needed to control five-story fins in the air pressures that resulted when planes flew 600 miles per hour. Special ejection seats had to be evolved that would explode the pilot into the air when trouble occurred. Besides a pressurized cabin, the bomber required a refrigeration system to overcome heat caused by the friction between the fast moving air and the metal of the plane's outer surfaces. Forty miles of electrical wiring comprised the nervous system of dials, levers, buttons, winking lights and magic boxes for automatic control.

Engineers knew that they had only scratched the surface of jet speed. Surprisingly, the faster a jet flew, the easier it became to produce more thrust. Even more surprising, the higher the plane flew, the less thrust it needed to move faster. It seemed possible to attain a staggering power and efficiency. The jet motor was perfected to 1,800 revolutions a minute, which permitted speeds of 650 miles an hour. Then came an unexpected barrier.

When experimental jet planes dove at speeds beyond 650 miles an hour, they began to vibrate dangerously. Strange and hidden forces struck the jet craft.

The rounded leading edge of the tapering fuselage of the jet fighter compressed the air in front of the plane into the hardness of a pumped-up bicycle tire. A cone-shaped air mass had to be pushed along with the expenditure of much power. Beyond 650 miles per hour at high altitudes the wave pushed further back and down, gripping the control surfaces in the rear, making them inoperable. The wave kept battering the wings, sometimes ripping them off. The pilot found himself helpless, unable to control the whirlwind. The plane plummeted into a nose dive.

A few survivors of such flights managed to reach lower altitudes and survive to tell the story. They provided a clue that solved the mystery. It was a phenomenon that Ernest

Mach had discovered in a photographic study of projectiles. He called it the sonic barrier because it always happened at the speed of sound. A shock wave was generated at 660 miles an hour, very high up. Near ground level a 760-mile speed was required to start the same kind of shock wave. Waves like giant pincers snapped down on wings to grip and im-mobilize the tail assembly at high altitudes, but at a lower altitude they did not reach the rudder and elevator, which a pilot must maneuver to land safely.

Once engineers saw the conelike wave in photographs made in wind tunnels, they began to try to figure out how to evade it. At first, they tried to slam through it with brute power. They created so revolutionary a design for the experimental X-1 rocket plane that it looked like a giant fifty caliber bullet. It was the first plane to be rocket-powered, burning a mix-ture of ethyl alcohol and liquid oxygen, consuming two tons of fuel a minute. When civilian test pilots refused $150,000 to test this "sure killer," Charles Yeager of the Air Force volunteered to risk his life. The X-1 was made strong enough to withstand the steel-hard, viselike grip of the shock wave and a force eighteen times the pull of gravity. Once past the buffeting of the ten-second barrier, the two and a half minute flight was smooth and wonderful even when its speed reached 900 miles an hour.

Then the engineers tried another method, redirection of the waves. They swept back the wings so that the shock waves would be swept off the wing tips at an angle that would not allow them to reach the tail assembly. Then the shock waves were dissipated even more by pinching the wings in the middle so that the waves took a roller coaster ride down, up and away. They could no longer get a paralyzing hold on the tail assembly and make it impossible for the pilot to maneuver and maintain complete control. Once this was done, there was no need to burst through the sonic barrier with a ten second shake-up. The jet plane need only slide through.

Fifteen experimental planes were tried out. The X-2 used stainless steel and razor sharp edges for its wings to cope with supersonic speed. The X-3 had a refrigerating system to reduce the heat generated when it went beyond a thousand miles an hour. The X-5 had swept back wings. The X-15 was made of the new wonder metal, titanium, far stronger and more heat-resistant than steel. Its rocket engines had twice as much horsepower as the largest aircraft carrier in the world. Fifty feet long, with a wing span of 22 feet, the X-15's goal was to attain 5,000 miles per hour. Each new model kept increasing its power punch and speed capability. The United States time table for future conquests of the air will depend on what the X-experimental planes are able to do. The ultimate goal is an aerospace plane—a blending of a space rocket and an airplane.

By 1956 the supersonic speed of bombers and fighters made them practically indistinguishable, each with about the same weight and the same operational ceiling. Both bombers and fighters could breeze along at 2,000 miles per hour. It was found that at such speeds, the boundary layer of air traveled with the aeroplane and raised the temperature of the metal to a dangerous level. At 1,370 miles per hour, the temperature soared to 250 degrees. At 2,050 miles per hour, the temperature shot to 650 degrees, beyond the melting point of aluminum. Engineers rushed to the rescue with a coating of tractable titanium, which was as light as aluminum but more resistant to heat. They created a honeycomb sandwich of stainless steel and ceramic molds to shield the fuel from the heat of its passageway.

So many new instruments were added that the pilot could no longer cope with his 150 dials and controls. So the instruments were joined to a computer whose lightning calculations were summarized in a few visual readings. Supersonic speed, in fact, created such complex control problems that the robot finally took over. With that a new horizon opened—the mis-

Cockpit of the *DC-9. Douglas Aircraft Co. Inc.*

sile, with no human aboard. It had its own propulsion system, its own navigational guidance, its own "homing" devices, and its own mechanical-electronic brain, sensitive to heat, light and changes in the magnetic field. The missile could do anything a fighter or bomber could do and with a speed they could never equal. This has given the military a new problem. Has the piloted fighting aircraft become obsolete? The size, range and maneuverability of military rockets has shifted progress in manned military aircraft. Controversy is still raging on what to do next.

Meanwhile, the one great boon to mankind in all of this is the improvement in airline passenger service that has resulted from military discoveries.

Airborne Multitudes

AIRLINES TODAY CARRY MORE PASSENGERS THAN BUSES AND railroads combined. The boom has come as a surprise to everyone except the visionaries who created the jet passenger liner. De Havilland was the first of the modern giants of aviation to foresee that a pressurized cabin far above the weather zone could provide a pleasant ride for everyone.

He had earned one fortune with his *Gypsy Moth*, the most popular of the British private planes. Military aircraft during the war brought him a second fortune. Then in 1949 when the first jet-propelled bomber flew from London to New York and back in one day, De Havilland decided to gamble his fortune on a jet passenger liner.

The first Comet was ready in May, 1952. It carried 48 passengers at 490 miles per hour and flew at 42,000 feet. There were no empty seats until the first of a series of disasters came in 1954. The Comet's certificate of airworthiness was then withdrawn. A full-scale test revealed the hidden fault. The compressed air within the cabin—warm, humidified, oxygenated and comfortable for the passengers—exerted enough pressure during stratospheric speed to blow out the windows and explode the jet. The structure enclosing the pressurized air was not strong enough. England had lost its role as the leader in civil aviation.

W. E. Boeing won the jet race for the U.S. A venturesome millionaire at thirty-four, Boeing learned to build airplanes in an abandoned Seattle boatyard. His biplane became the first efficient airmail carrier, winning for him the San Francisco-Chicago route. By 1930 he had built the first plane with a retractable landing gear. His 1933 ten-passenger Boeing-247 was the first twin-engined commercial transport plane in the United States. His 1938 Stratoliner was the first transport with a pressurized cabin. He spent $275,000 of his own money to build the Flying Fortress that won so great a name in World War II. And the Boeing Corporation gambled sixteen million dollars to develop the 707 Jet that revolutionized commercial air travel all over the world. It was first airborne on July 15, 1954. Its huge rotors spun 13,000 times a minute. The fires in its engines consumed 1,000 gallons of kerosene

Boeing 707, long range jetliner. *The Boeing Co.*

an hour—an amount capable of heating 1,000 five-room houses. The 20,000 pound blast that roared out of the jet engines could knock down a man standing 150 feet away. The 707 flew eight miles up, the limit for engines that depend on air.

Today, there are almost as many airlines as there are countries, and almost all of them fly jets. In few places of the world is the huge shape of the jet liner unfamiliar, so interwoven has air travel become in the daily life of man. This will become even more true in the future, when every town will have its airport, just as it has its railroad station and its bus terminal.

Aviation is the fastest growing industry in the United States. It has increased yearly at the rate of fourteen per cent. It now boasts over 20,000 firms and 1,300,000 employees. More than 100,000 private planes and 9,000 airline planes crowd the skies. The passenger plane has become as indispensable as the corner bank—a reality that would have seemed incredible fifteen years ago.

Airports have sprung up like dandelions. The most important are those that serve international flights and handle 200 million passengers each year. New York has 22 million passengers yearly. Chicago's airport sees a landing and take-off every 50 seconds. Los Angeles has 132,000 employees in airport-related jobs.

The 107 jet ports around the world are microcosms already taking on an international tone all their own. They have duty free merchandise, restaurants, bars, control towers, runways, radar and radio installations, and enormous buildings to provide speedy transition from ground to air. These air cities are growing faster than the metropolises that surround them. Their restaurants, garages, hospitals and hotels offer a glimpse of the comforts the next century will bring.

These centers of the airborne multitudes, with their electronic miracles that bring order out of the chaos of traffic, have already entered the next century. The science of avionics —the electronic control of aviation—began with the radio, and went on to the radar and anti-aircraft gunnery of World War II. It moved forward with the development of the Decca Navigation System, which directs the landing and launching of aircraft in airports. Three meters identify and a rolling chart register the progress of arriving and departing aircraft in relation to the ground.

This robot brain has grown more complex and more subtle as traffic has grown more complicated. To help radar operators handle more planes, a new electronic instrument was developed. The "transponder" is a type of radio transmitter that identifies a plane and its altitude. This information races down a radar beam into a ground computer; a screen then displays the plane's flight number, its assigned altitude and its true altitude. Dotted lines shoot across the screen to show where the plane will be located eight minutes later, a forewarning of possible collisions.

But even this type of transmission is slow and outdated compared with a computer display system that permits automatic devices in the plane itself to transfer to the computer changes in altitude, direction and speed second by second. The controller on the ground can see at a glance, from a picture that shows all planes in his area, exactly what is there, their relation to each other and to his station. Possible trouble can be eliminated before it even has a chance to start.

This seems almost to eliminate the need for a pilot and perhaps even for a controller on the ground. As robot communicates with robot, no humans are needed. This will be even more the case when the new Instrument Landing System (ILS) becomes universal, for this device can land a plane even in zero visibility.

The one great irritant in this bright picture is the congestion of ground traffic around the airport. Frequently, it takes longer to reach the airport of a city than it does to fly between two relatively distant cities. There was a time after World War II when everyone was sure the helicopter would provide the needed door-to-door transportation, instead of the tortuous bumper-to-bumper ride on the highways. It hasn't worked that way.

The helicopter was born out of a need for safety rather than for speed. In fact, all through the nineteenth century, the helicopter was more the target of dreamers and experimenters than the airplane. It was considered the only safe kind of air transport. The first successful helicopter was made by a man who had an airplane accident in his youth and who vowed to devote his life to the problem of making flying foolproof against accidents. Don Juan de la Cierva of Spain hit upon the idea of the free windmill above an airplane. It was a kind of rotor that would go on spinning and generating lift, even with the engine power cut off. His autogiro, the predecessor of the helicopter, was first flown in 1923.

The best of pilots knows that there is always the danger of a sneak punch from the wind. A sudden vertical air current, thought of until recently as an "air pocket," can instantly throw the plane out of the stable angle at which it is flying. The blow can be so powerful, and the plane tossed into such an excessive angle, that the plane can plunge out of control.

Similarly the skilled pilot and the airplane are both helpless in the face of stalling speed; the plunge and the spin follow. It is the most lethal of all types of accidents. But a plane with a rotating wing has a magic circle of safety. Whatever the situation, loss of engine power or a blow from a vertical thermal, the rotor continues to be rotated by the wind and the flying machine can descend gently to a soft landing. The rotor acts as a mechanical parachute.

In the beginning Cierva faced the same problems that had plagued helicopter designers for a hundred years. The rotor blade advanced rapidly as it revolved forward and slowly as it turned back, creating a mishmash of forces that twisted his flying machine in all directions. How could he equalize the lift of the blades? He solved the problem to a great extent by separating the blades, so that they worked independently from one another. He gave each of the blades individual movement within the hub. He hinged the blades so that they were free to rise and fall as well as rotate. The retreating blade fell from the hub and it moved faster, helping it to catch up to the faster speed of the advancing blade.

To start his rotor spinning on the ground, Cierva connected it with the engine. The blades, however, exerted no lift, because they cut the air at zero pitch, simply knifing the air. As he taxied to windward Cierva declutched the engine from the rotor shaft. At the same time, he twisted the rotor blades to an angle offering them resistance to the wind. The rotor blades thus became a free windmill rotated by the wind, while the propellers in the rear, powered by the engine, continued to push the plane forward. For the first time, man was flying with a complete assurance of safety.

Cierva was killed in an airplane crash while he was on a business trip to England. Further developments in rotary flight were left to other hands. Pitcairn took the autogiro-evolution another step forward with vertical jump take off. In 1937 Heinrich Focke of Germany made George Cayley's convertiplane design of 1843 a reality. His flying machine had twin contra-rotating rotors, mounted on either side of the fuselage, with a rear propeller for horizontal flight. It became the first flying machine capable of hovering.

Two years later Igor Sikorsky demonstrated his classic helicopter that advanced the dream of safe flying still further. His VS-300 could fly in any direction. This was done simply by varying the angles at which the rotor blades met the wind. To fly forward, the angle of each blade was increased automatically to the utmost pitch while it was passing over the tail of the aircraft. Then the pitch of the rotor blade decreased as it moved towards the front. In this way, the greatest lift came from the rear, causing a forward push.

The pilot needed only to reverse the angle of the blades to have the greatest pitch occur at the front, causing the helicopter to fly backwards. To fly towards the right or left, it was only necessary to increase the pitch of the rotor blades on the side opposite the direction the pilot wished to go. A small, raised rear propeller that was spun in a direction opposite to that of the rotor blade prevented a torque effect, the tendency of the body of the machine to spin around in the same direction as the rotor blades.

The complexity of Sikorsky's helicopter explains why it took more than ten years to perfect. All three of the rotor blades, which are really the wings of the plane, had to be given variable pitch, so it was possible to change the angle of the blades while they continued rotating at a constant number of revolutions per minute. A system of rods and levers changed the pitch of the blades in an automatic time sequence. This kept the plane headed in the proper direction.

A main rotor that permits individual movement of the blades from the hub in both a lateral and vertical direction is called an articulated rotor. It is the hub itself that does the seesawing and the rocking, the vertical and lateral movements necessary to balance the unequal forces.

Only an engineer can understand the formidable problems of helicopter flight. It requires twice as much power as an airplane for equal performance. It is more difficult to drive, especially when stick, rudder, throttle and pitch control lever have to be worked simultaneously with the use of both hands and feet simply to hover. The rotor requires at least 100 revolutions a minute, bringing noisy vibrations. It

Sikorsky VS 300 Helicopter. *Smithsonian Institution.*

will be a long time before anyone will build a helicopter the
mass market can afford. The dream of buying a helicopter
for the price of a car and flying from backyard to office roof
has faded away. Today the cheapest helicopter costs about
$25,000.

However, the helicopter is freer than the airplane from
possible disaster, and this fact alone has given it an endless
series of uses. It has become the handmaiden of the oil industry in off-shore drilling; it is the vehicle used to reach inaccessible spots; it is a lifesaver in jungle warfare.

The rise of the turbine engine, with its high ratio of horsepower to weight, has made possible helicopters that are faster,
easier to fly, less costly to operate and practically unlimited in
size and load-carrying capacity. Sikorsky is now building, at
two million dollars each, *Flying Cranes*, which can land ten

tons of cargo in a space smaller than their own shadow. The Hughes *300* helicopter has a 200-mile range and a 14,000 foot ceiling to cross mountains. Boeing's Vertol Chinooks can carry 44 infantrymen into battle at speeds of up to 150 miles per hour.

Variations in the make-up of helicopters include hollow blades whose tips are used as combustion chambers. The burning gases spin them after the fashion of a rotary lawn sprinkler. Then there is a helicopter with twin rotors, placed one just behind the other with blades intermeshed, so as to reduce the area of the spinning position. The blades spin in opposite directions to eliminate torque.

But nothing can disguise the fact that helicopters are limited in speed. Their top speed is about 250 miles per hour. The forward spin of the blade, about 400 miles an hour, has to be added to the speed of the machine. If the sum of these two speeds reaches 700 miles per hour, the flying machine will encounter the sonic barrier with all its buffeting and mishmash of forces. The limitation to speed in the helicopter has brought engineers to look elsewhere for an air bus design. The Vertical Take-Off machine (VTOL) might be the answer.

The inventor of the new vertical take-off machine was Dr. A.A. Griffith, one of England's great creative minds in the area of flight. He began by tackling the problem of lowering the airplane's stalling speed—the point of low speed at which a plane is liable to plunge. He knew that the key was to be found in the control of air circulation around a wing. If the air next to the skin of the plane becomes turbulent, all becomes turbulent. Griffith invented a many-slotted wing on which the engine sucked the boundary layer of air through the slots. The air moved smoothly and the stalling speed was lowered from 115 miles per hour to 73 miles per hour; the speed of ground approach for landing from 150 to 93 miles per hour.

The capacity to control air flow increased for Griffith when the air compressor of the jet engine came into use. Such a turbine was a ready source of high pressure air, perfect for sucking and for blowing. The new air blowing capacity led to a revolutionary idea. Griffith deflected the high pressure air from the engine to the edges of wings, giving the jet plane added thrust. By sucking in the air through small holes in the wing, he gave the jet plane added lift.

Then Griffith conceived the idea of lifting a new kind of plane upward by airblast alone, generated by a pair of jet engines over which a pilot had his seat. This type of flying machine had no wings, fuselage or tail, and came to be known as the *Flying Bedstead*. Vertical jet ducts blasted the air downward for lift and thrust, and compressed air expelled from nozzles at the right and left balanced the machine. The bedstead performed with spectacular success.

Dr. Griffith proved that it was possible to sit upon the engine thrust, raise himself on it, hover on it, descend on it and even fly forward with it. Compressed air from nozzles took the place of control surfaces. Riding on a cushion of air opened up a vast new horizon for flight. It brought into being the hydroplane on water and the high speed train that flies on a ribbon of compressed air less than one inch thick.

Experiments using the flying bedstead principle for vertical take-off and landing of aircraft have been performed in major aviation centers. As early as 1955, the Bell Convertiplane in the United States combined the features of the helicopter with the conventional propeller plane. Rotors were mounted on the wing tips to give vertical take-off; when the wings were tilted for horizontal flight, the rotors acted like propellers.

By 1957 England had the first forty-eight passenger air bus cruising at 185 miles per hour for intercity travel, the *Fairey Rotodyne*. During forward flight its rotor blades "freewheeled" like an autogiro to help the stub wings in maintaining lift. Air was piped in through the hollow rotor blades and forced out through the tips, which acted like ram jet units.

We are still in the middle of research and development for the rotary wing aircraft. As it stands today, the helicopter and the vertical lift aircraft are competing with each other for the vast untapped air bus market of the future. In the next generation the Northeast Corridor from Boston to Washington will be one vast megalopolis of 250 million people. Similar sprawls of cities will connect areas in the Great Lakes and in Southern California. To get the masses of passengers in these areas from place to place, new railroads like Japan's high speed 150 mile per hour trains and France's 250 mile per hour railway cars will be racing over cushions of air. But people will also be demanding an air bus service. The United States and Western Germany have launched a half billion dollar program to solve the problems of the interurban bus.

Engineers predict that the air bus of the future will have two separate propulsion systems: one will lift it straight up in the air, the other will give it added push after the desired altitude has been reached—something that Cayley had foretold in 1843.

A 400 mile per hour speed will be necessary to attract customers, and this, in itself, involves special problems. A rotor cannot develop such speed. It will break to pieces if it is speeded up past its critical point. The additional thrust of an airplane is necessary to get the machines to move faster. Up to 340 miles per hour, the speed of the rotor will be reduced while craft speed is increased. Beyond 340 miles per hour, engineers are planning to stop the rotor altogether and fold it back. The air bus will then fly up to 500 miles per hour as a fixed wing plane.

These new plans entail surprising transformation in design. The teetering or flapping hinges of helicopters will be abandoned. They demand too much constant control by pilots.

Instead, a new type of rigid blade rotor is being created. A control gyroscope, gimbaled atop the rotor mast, will take over. It will stabilize the entire machine and be capable of changing the pitch of the rotor blades to give direction to the aircraft. The pilot will have far less trouble operating this machine than the conventional helicopter. A sixty passenger version of this fast and convenient gyrodyne points to the practical airbus of tomorrow.

However, the noise problem still has to be faced. Possibly, compressed air might be pumped into the airbus from the ground to start its large rotor blade whirling to take-off speed and thus make possible a lighter engine with less noise and vibration. There might be other problems. One need only imagine a thirty ton helibus, built to hold 150 passengers and with a downward blasting force of thirty tons. With friction eliminated under the constant blast fan near the ground, the helibus might tend to skid, throwing grit and grime in all directions.

Because of such handicaps, Sikorsky claims that his *Giant Crane* will be the best bet for interurban travel. The sky crane could pick up, carry and deposit crowded buses, passengers and all, from downtown to the airport. A taxi service by helicopter has to be subsidized to pay its way at competitive prices to reach an airport. Only about two thousand helicopters are in civilian use and average sales do not go beyond five hundred a year.

In contrast, the vertical lift aircraft is forging ahead. It has the edge on speed, a ready source of high pressure air in its jet turbine and a wide range of low to high speeds. It is expected that air cushion landing will eventually eliminate the undercarriage altogether and all the hydraulic and mechanical gear that goes with it. Wing surfaces could become increasingly smaller since the wind blast of compressed air alone can lift the rotary wing craft at low speed and support it in fast, cruising flight. Since speed is the pacemaker, the rotary wing helibus is bound to serve the airborne multitudes of the future, phasing out the helicopter.

A preview of this kind of airbus can be seen in the American military swing-wing *XC-142 A*, expected to be in service in the 1970's. It is designed to take off vertically with a four-ton payload and cruise at 400 miles per hour. It will be capable of hovering for ten minutes. It will use jet blasts as well as propellers.

Toward the Edge of Space and Beyond

IN ALL THE EXCITEMENT OVER AIRPLANES, ZEPPELINS, JETS, and VTOLS, balloons have almost been forgotten by the general public. But not by the scientists. Balloons have played a little known role in the exploration of the upper atmosphere. They have alerted scientists to the fact that oxygen bottles or masks are useless about ten miles up. There is so little air pressure that an air compressor is necessary to force oxygen into the lungs. From balloon findings scientists have been able to calculate that at about thirteen miles up, fluids in the body will begin to boil.

Scientists have also learned that breathable air extends to only two miles above the surface of the earth. Farther up, five great wind circles engulf the globe from the North to the South Pole, moving in alternate directions. Anywhere from two to eight miles up, temperature changes become violent, ranging from 110 degrees below zero to 160 degrees above. There can be calm one day and shrieking 230 miles per hour winds the next. Jet streams tear around the globe at a terrific 300 miles per hour. The balloonist who lifted his pressurized gondola twelve miles up was the first to see the black darkness of space. At this altitude, rubberized cloth barely supported its own weight and could not go any higher.

Just in time for the higher flights needed to bring in the jet age, technology provided a new miracle material. Polyethelene can hold helium without leakage for a long time and is not affected by frigidity, torrid heat, or ultra-violet rays. A polyethelene balloon can hold ten million cubic feet of helium, support a dowmetal gondola, and rise to a height of thirty or more miles. This made it possible to have a laboratory in the sky and brought the balloon to new importance.

Since 1947 *Project Skyhook* has launched more than 1500 sky laboratories, which carry instruments up as high as 145,000 feet. The balloon is now soaring towards even greater prominence by mapping and photographing the weather system around the earth. Plans are moving rapidly towards a worldwide pattern of total weather forecasting.

Thus far, only about ten percent of the earth is covered by balloon gatherers of information. But very soon the United Nations World Weather Watch will be able to predict weather everywhere two weeks in advance. Data will be collected from points no more than 300 miles apart and at many levels of the atmosphere. It will be a system of 10,000 balloons at levels from 20,000 up to 80,000 feet. They will have instant communication with Nimbus satellites that will evaluate the data and feed information into three computer centers: Washington, Moscow and Melbourne. The Northern Hemisphere alone will require ten billion computations within a single day.

Even while the upper atmosphere is being explored, the configuration of the airplane is being studied for the coming higher speeds at the higher altitudes. The swing toward delta (triangular) shape wings began with the creative thinking of Geoffrey Hill of England in 1930. It occurred to Hill that the fuselage-tailpiece lever might be a wasteful way to obtain stability and control in an aircraft. Why not get the same lever effects by sweeping the wings sharply back? The tips of the wings, instead of the tailpiece, could provide stability and control. Each small tip of his swept-back wings could be turned up or down. When they were turned together, they acted as elevators; when they were turned separately, they acted as ailerons.

Hill's swept-back wing design was not of vital importance until supersonic speed made it essential. For a time his design was swallowed up and forgotten in variations of new patents. In 1945 Wallis patented the delta wing as one large piece. In 1950 another British engineer, Bayne, took out a patent to swing two such triangular wings back and forth in a variable sweep.

Today the major controversy in aerodynamics is between the fixed wing and the variable wing for supersonic flight. John Stack, who was responsible for the *X-1* design and the variable sweep wing for the *F-111*, feels certain that two different wing arrangements are needed for low speed and super-

First flight of the F-111A, December 21, 1964.
U. S. Air Force Photo.

sonic speed. He advocates taking off with wings that are straight out and then sweeping them back on pivots as the plane picks up speed.

Kelly Johnson of Lockheed favors the fixed delta wing. He claims that a small second delta wing close to the fuselage can create a swirling of air above the large delta wing to provide the extra lift necessary for low speed. Why, then, add the weight and complexity of a heavy mechanical pivot to swing wings back and forth?

The differing opinions about wing shape indicate that aerodynamic theory is still in a state of flux. *The Scientific American* has even rallied amateur contestants to innovate new shapes for paper planes. The shape of future planes may go through many transformations.

Aviation is now in the midst of the longest continuous evolution in the history of any industry. American subsonic jet passenger planes had captured the world market. A Boeing 707, for example, becomes airborne every 13 seconds somewhere on earth. But this dominant position for the American-built planes has been threatened in the realm of the supersonic transport. The Concorde, a British-French undertaking, and the Russian TU-144 may capture the passenger market for the future. Though neither is as large or as fast as the United States supersonic being built by Boeing, they will be ready to fly sooner.

New supersonic transports will have to win public favor with the latest safety devices. In a crash fire and smoke are still the major menace, sweeping through a plane with frightening rapidity. It is now possible to convert fuel to less inflammable jelly within seconds of impact. It is also possible to have explosive charges open up sections of a cabin instantly for quick evacuation. A sprinkler system may have to be provided to quell the incredible heat of aircraft fire so as to allow a maximum of ten minutes for escape. A new kind of mask can permit passengers to breath their own air for eight

Mockup of Boeing SST, the plane of the 1970's.
The Boeing Co.

Diagram of the Boeing SST. *The Boeing Co.*

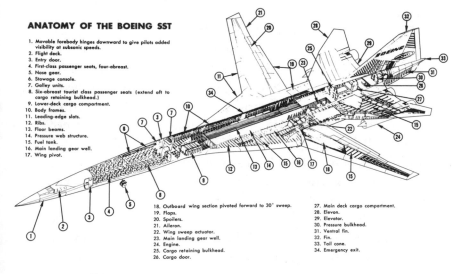

ANATOMY OF THE BOEING SST

1. Movable forebody hinges downward to give pilots added visibility at subsonic speeds.
2. Flight deck.
3. Entry door.
4. First-class passenger seats, four-abreast.
5. Nose gear.
6. Stowage console.
7. Galley units.
8. Six-abreast tourist class passenger seats (extend aft to cargo retaining bulkhead.)
9. Lower-deck cargo compartment.
10. Body frames.
11. Leading-edge slats.
12. Ribs.
13. Floor beams.
14. Pressure web structure.
15. Fuel tank.
16. Main landing gear well.
17. Wing pivot.

18. Outboard wing section pivoted forward to 30° sweep.
19. Flaps.
20. Spoilers.
21. Aileron.
22. Wing sweep actuator.
23. Main landing gear well.
24. Engine.
25. Cargo retaining bulkhead.
26. Cargo door.

27. Main deck cargo compartment.
28. Elevon.
29. Elevator.
30. Pressure bulkhead.
31. Ventral fin.
32. Fin.
33. Tail cone.
34. Emergency exit.

minutes to avoid smoke asphyxiation. With 350 passengers supersonic jets will need every possible safety device.

In developing faster and faster planes, engineers are faced with all kinds of new problems. The outside surface of the fuselage will heat up to 450 degrees at 1750 miles per hour. The titanium skin must be made flexible enough to stretch as much as sixteen inches under such heat. The electronic controls will have to be made more foolproof. The pilot will have only four seconds to make an emergency change at supersonic speed as compared with ten seconds for present jet liners. Then again, the pilot, sitting forty feet above the wheels, must cope with a landing speed fifty miles an hour faster than conventional jets. The biggest headache is the sonic booms such planes create flying at supersonic speeds. This has yet to be coped with.

All the same, speed is the pacemaker of progress in the air today. Thirty years ago the Pan American Clipper took two hours to fly from Washington to New York. Supersonic planes in the same period of time will fly from Washington to London. And they will be able to carry twenty times as many passengers.

The supersonics will do for the Pacific what jets have done for the Atlantic. They will revolutionize business and pleasure travel markets. In the next decade the air corridors of the world will cary 360 million passengers a year. Young people and venturesome older tourists, especially, will make travel the major recreation of the new age. Those who do not need speed will be flying subsonic at reduced fares. Boeing is already displaying models of its planned 747 which will carry 490 passengers, and Lockheed is moving ahead with an incredible triple deck that will seat 902.

Meanwhile, great strides are being made in air cargo transport. The Soviet *AN-22* will hold 80 tons of cargo. And the U.S. military is demanding a plane capable of lifting 700,000 pounds. Needless to say such planes will also have commercial possibilities.

Air freight volume already exceeds passenger volume. Costs are 21 cents per unit load, compared to six cents by truck, but the gap will be closed when the giant cargo planes go into operation in the 1970s. Before long we will see a new system of containers, airport automation and data processing equipment to speed up freight transfer with a rapidity almost inconceivable today. Even the Boeing 727 is capable of converting from passengers to freight in eight minutes.

We need only examine the military plans for aircraft to realize that designs are being prepared for future speeds up to 15,000 miles per hour. The hypersonic transport is rehearsing in the wings, preparing for the 1980s. The HST will fly a hundred miles up, reach rocket speed, and cross the United States in ten minutes or blast to any part of the earth in less than an hour.

Military planes already in existence are like science fiction dreams. The United States F-111 can fly at treetop level at supersonic speed, and it can fly at six miles a minute and make turns so fast that pilots have to endure six times the pull of gravity. Its Terrain Following Radar (TFR) gives the F-111 the skill to dip in valleys and skim over peaks even in zero visibility. Its Inertial Navigation System (INS) lets the pilot know precisely where he is in relation to his take-off point, target, and return base. Its nervous system is so finely tuned that the slightest fluctuation in direction or speed will activate rudder, flaps, and elevators simultaneously to adjust for pitch, roll or yaw.

Though the F-111 is an engineering miracle, it still lacks the range necessary for military purposes. Hence, the XB-70 and its twin, the XB-70B, were built to fly for a distance of 12,000 miles. The computer alone for each of these planes weighed three tons upon installation. It provides 20,000 readings a second from 1,170 data sensors, registers among other items strain, temperature, flutter, pressures, roll, pitch, yaw and deceleration. Before the start of a flight the pilots must check 260 items on eighteen pages. In flight this giant fighter-bomber can cruise half way around the world at 2,000 miles per hour. Only the XB-70B survives today. The XB-70 was destroyed when one of six planes that were photographing it in flight got too close and touched one of the air monsters' two huge, vertical fins. One touch was enough. Both planes crashed.

The experimental X-15 has flown at more than 4,300 miles per hour, and, using it for a pattern, the military is planning a new, all-purpose combination fighter-bomber with a speed of 3,000 miles per hour and more.

The experimental XB-70A. *U. S. Air Force Photo.*

The ultimate goal is the aerospace plane, a marriage of missile and airplane, capable of rising from the ground to orbital flight at satellite speed and returning to home base completely under the control of the pilot. Though still only a projection, science has developed almost all of the necessary components. At a speed of Mach 8, more than 5,000 miles per hour, the boundary layer of air next to the skin of the hypersonic plane is no longer the air we know. Its very molecular structure breaks down and generates temperatures that cause even titanium to soften, stretch and flow, or as engineers say "creep." To tolerate temperatures up to 6,000 degrees, new metals are being spun out of carbonized thread and the "whiskers" of boron. Boron weighs less than aluminum but has a hardness second only to that of a diamond. Liquid hydrogen will circulate at 423 degrees below zero against the inside of the boron skin to make the missile plane a "flying icebox." The cockpit with all its groupings of illustrated panels will be like a teaching machine, telling the pilot what to do as simply and clearly as possible.

Three engines will power this hypersonic plane. It will take off with a turbojet. Twenty miles up a ramjet engine will take over. Burnt up gases will spew out of the rear of the engine to propel the plane up to 8,400 miles per hour. Tons of air will be sent into electronic machines that will break it down into its components, to be liquified and stored within tanks for use later as refrigerants and fuels. When the atmosphere becomes too thin, the rocket engine will take over for the final leap into space. Thirty miles up a rocket blast will launch the plane at 15,000 miles per hour into a suborbital trajectory.

When flying at 250 miles per minute through a weightless void, airplane controls can no longer be used. The Inertial Guidance System on its gyro platform will do the automatic steering. At the reëntry point reaction jets on the top of the nose and the wing tips will drive the plane towards the landing point. The plane will glide down through the atmosphere at a gentle angle. At about 40,000 feet above the ground the autopilot or the pilot can steer by rudder control to a typical jet passenger landing.

New Dreams for a New Age

ALTHOUGH MOST UNIDENTIFIED FLYING OBJECTS HAVE BEEN identified as natural phenomena such as cloud formations, ball lightning, meteors, migrating birds, and temperature inversions, scientists are still baffled by the intelligent descriptions of saucer-shaped flying machines that move from hovering to meteoric speed within one instant. Whatever these "flying saucers" may be, they present a challenge to the imagination of the engineer. To achieve a hovering position one second and the speed of a meteor the next or to make right angle turns at supersonic speeds is a much dreamed of achievement. The flying saucer craze has inspired new designs for future aircraft, especially a giant saucer-shaped craft for interplanetary travel, to be rocketed by an exhaust of subatomic particles.

As it now stands, an atomic power plant is not feasible for aircraft. The need for heavy shielding against atomic radiation has been too great a stumbling block. Perhaps the giant accelerator scheduled to be completed in 1972 may disclose the clue that will make it possible to build an electron gas mirror that could surround and insulate the five million degree heat necessary for atomic fusion. If so, the world will find unlimited energy available from the water that covers two-thirds of the earth. Engineers have gone ahead on the basis that such energy will become available.

They have imagined a half-mile hemisphere floating evenly on a cushion of air. The undersurface of this giant flying saucer will have a circle of twenty-four nozzles from which jets of hot air will explode, keeping the saucer balanced over a body of water. Lateral jets will push the saucer across the water with air cushion softness, gathering speed to get it airborne.

At 30,000 feet up, reducing plants will begin collecting water from clouds and moist air to fill tanks with liquefied oxygen and hydrogen, to be used later as refrigerants and propellant fuels. Rocket power will take the ship out of the atmosphere and into orbital velocity. In space, automatic devices will switch the power to the nuclear engine, whose exhaust will blast out the subatomic particles that will propel the ship on its comfortable fifty hour trip to Mars. Nearing the planet, the flying saucer will match the planet's velocity, steering toward the target point. Air blasts will settle it down to a soft, vertical landing.

The huge size of this flying saucer will be possible because of the fusion engine, a perpetual heat source constantly transforming and recirculating the elements in a cycle of liquid, gas, and ionization. The saucer shape, like an immense parachute, will be best for the soft landing by downward jet.

The promise of the future is most staggering, however, when one considers possible fuels. The chemical combustion to transfer matter into energy is, at best, only one ten-billionth of what is theoretically possible. The jump from gasoline to rocket fuel, important as it was, cannot compare to the change from chemical fuel to ionized particles. Once we are able to control the explosion of particle and anti-particle, the velocity of an aircraft may reach almost the speed of light.

Another possibility in achieving speed and maneuverability is gravity. The prevailing scientific opinion about gravity is that it does not change with temperature, light, darkness, electricity, magnetism or any known kind of wave. Different materials are equally accelerated by the pull of gravity. In short, "gravity" is a word we use to describe one of the characteristics of the geometry of space.

But some scientists argue that the oscillations in a gravitational field are analagous to electro-magnetic waves in an electro-magnetic field. The basic unit of this gravitational energy, whether wave or particle, is called a graviton. What it is, or whether it actually exists or not, is a matter of speculation.

Whatever gravity is, however, the ultimate in transportation could be achieved by gravity control. By controlling gravity, we would be able to accelerate in any direction as fast as we desired without feeling any mechanical stress or force. The dream of flight that began with flapping wings, soared with gas bags, whirled and blasted with gas combustion and is now evolving to flight propelled by subatomic particles, could reach its greatest potential by paralyzing its greatest antagonist, the pull of gravity.

Santos Dumont has a special place in aviation history because he demonstrated in his life the pleasures of personal flying. His last years were spent trying to create a flying machine that could be comfortably strapped on one's back. The dream of personal flying has now reached mass proportions with the small plane. And more than a million flying enthusiasts are now cavorting through the air with gliders, flying chair gyrocopters, jet belts, soaring sailways, and skydiving parachutes. The soaring sailway, a crescent parachute, may take the place of snow-skiing for daring sportsmen of the future. The round-belly sky sled is inspiring Project Near

Earth Rescue Operation (NERO) to bring back stranded astronauts and may develop as a thrilling space sport in the future.

Flying jet belts are limited to military use, but they promise to become universal. The fiberglass corset fits the back and hips of the operator. A control stick changes flight direction. The pilot controls pitch and roll with his body. The power source is hydrogen peroxide, compressed into a gas generator, and released as steam to provide the thrust to propel a man.

At present more than thousands of civilians have taken to gyrocopters as a sport. This one-seater helicopter is barely eight feet long and can be described as a flying chair. It is equipped with a pusher engine, one rudder, one rotor blade and a single seat with a steering stick. It flies at thirty miles per hour.

The one man gyro-glider.
Individual transportation for the future?

The most sensational thrill personal flight can offer is sky-diving. Hurtling down towards the earth at 125 miles per hour free as a bird can be "like no other experience on earth." The parachute has become so perfected and skydiving so popular that the 100,000 enthusiasts are beginning to worry airplane pilots.

It is possible for motorless gliders to take advantage of the variable movements of wind to make long distance flights of more than five hundred miles. The solitary glider can float in updrafts from cloud to cloud in absolute silence, except for the sound of the wind. The birdmen of today use the clouds as stairways to the upper air and speak of vultures and eagles soaring side by side with them. Low speed flight is a relatively unexplored field. The dream persists that the future will bring a kind of personal glider capable of taking vacationers on a long distance jaunt across the United States.

The very rapidity of our technical advancements is creating anxious thoughts about the future. Will it all end the way E. M. Forster describes it in his classic science fiction story *The Machine Stops?* Forster imagines a world in which man will be living in a comfortable, cellular, underground room. Each cell of this future gigantic beehive receives hot, tasty meals, created by alchemical laboratories. Each tenant possesses a crystal ball, which requires only a knowing touch to put him in communication with anyone on earth or flash any desired entertainment on the wall. He need only step out to the end of a corridor to catch the scheduled flight of a winged car of unlimited power that will transport him anywhere on the globe. This all-weather, automatic flying machine rises like an elevator to the sky, landing and lifting off on its precisely scheduled stops from city to city. Its speed oustrips the pace of the sun, but in the book this flying wonder makes its rounds without pilots or passengers. "What was the good of going to Peking, when it was just like Shrewsbury?"

Other writers of science fiction bring us a more delightful forecast. They tell us that free-as-a-bird, personal flight will offer a release of the spirit, a symbol of escape from the limitations of an earth-bound existence. Forrester dreams of men flying through the air on will power alone. Stapledon imagines evolution developing organic wings for man. Both describe the beautiful, pure joy of flowing and effortless zooming of birdlike gliding.

In a future that is nearer to us than World War I, mining, agriculture, manufacturing and transport will be processed by the mere touch of appropriate buttons. Around the next corner are private beam television conversations around the world; molecular, genetic engineering for healthy minds in healthy bodies; and cheap pleasure aircraft that can become the most popular of sports.

Man's personal flying machine could be simplified to the shape of an umbrella with little jet points. He would need only to open his umbrella to have it tune in on high frequency beams, which would give him the power to disport himself with the freedom of a bird or an angel. Let this be the happy apex of an evolution that began with the clumsy and fatal attempt of Icarus to wing through the air on a flapping glider, rather than the drabness of a too uniform world or the horror of a world-ending air war.

Further Reading

LIGHTER THAN AIR

Vaeth, J. Gordon. *Two Hundred Miles Up*. New York: Ronald Press, 1955

Poole, Lynn. *Ballooning in the Space Age*. New York: Whittlesey House, 1958

Rolt, Lionel T. C. *The Aeronauts, a History of Ballooning*. New York: Walker, 1966

HISTORY OF FLIGHT

Lindbergh, Charles A. *The Spirit of St. Louis*. New York: Scribners, 1957

Taylor, John W. R. *A Picture History of Flight*. London: Hulton, 1959

Gibbs-Smith, Charles H. *The Aeroplane*. London: H. M. Stationery Office, 1960

Duke, Neville and Lanchberry, Edward, eds. *The Saga of Flight*. New York: John Day, 1961

Donovan, Frank. *The Early Eagles*. New York: Dodd, Mead, 1962

Bonney, Walter T. *The Heritage of Kitty Hawk*. New York: W. W. Norton, 1962

The American Heritage History of Flight. New York: American Heritage, 1962

Canby, Courtlandt. *A History of Flight*. New York: Hawthorn, 1963

Garber, Paul E. *National Aircraft Collection*. Washington, D.C.: Smithsonian Institution, 1965

Mason, Herbert Molloy. *Bold Men, Far Horizons*. New York: J. B. Lippincott Co., 1966

MODERN AIRCRAFT

Ross, Frank. *Young People's Book of Jet Propulsion*. New York: Lothrop, Lee & Shepard, 1954

Cooke, David C. *Jet and Rocket Planes that Made History*. New York: Putnam, 1961

Cooke, David C. *Helicopters that Made History*. New York: Putnam, 1963

Grover, Heiman. *Jet Pioneers*. New York: Duell, Sloan & Pierce, 1963

Caidin, Martin. *Aviation and Space Medicine*. New York: E. P. Dutton, 1962

Caidin, Martin. *The Long Arm of America*. New York: E. P. Dutton, 1963

Jablonski, Edward. *Flying Fortress*. New York: Doubleday and Co., 1965

Stambler, Irwin. *Supersonic Transport*. New York: G. P. Putnam's Sons, 1965

SIMPLE TECHNICAL EXPLANATIONS

Blacker, Robert D. *Basic Aeronautical Science and Principles of Flight*. American Technical Society, 1958

Gibbs-Smith, C. H. *Sir George Cayley's Aeronautics*. London: Her Majesty's Stationery Office, 1962

Naylor, J. L. and Ower, F. *Aviation: Its Technical Development*. Philadelphia: Dufour Editions, 1965
Stewart, Oliver. *Aviation: The Creative Ideas*. New York: Praeger, 1966

IMAGINATIVE LITERATURE ON FLIGHT

Murchie, Guy. *Song of the Sky*. Boston: Houghton Mifflin, 1954
Verne, Jules. *Clipper of the Clouds*. Associated Booksellers, 1962
———. *Master of the World*. Associated Booksellers, 1962
———. *The City in the Sahara*. Associated Booksellers, 1962
Wells, H. G. *The War in the Air*. New York: Dover Publications, Inc., 1963

Index

Academy of Science, Paris, 12-15, 17, 31, 34-5, 112
Ader, Clement, 122-4, 137, 160-1
Aeveon (balloon), 67-8
Aerial photography, 85
Aexo Club (French), 164, 170, 173-4, 177-82
Aerodromes (Langley's), 126-7, 135-6
aerodynamics, principles of, 4, 6, 36-8, 39-46, 49-50, 52, 56, 58, 71-3, 77, 87, 107, 110, 114, 119, 120-1, 124, 126, 132-3, 166, 215, 244, 250-2
Aeronautical Society of Great Britain, 104, 106, 108
aerospace plane, 257-8
aileron, 109, 133, 198, 251
air bus, 245-7; helibus, 247-8
Air freight, 254-5
aircraft carriers, 224
Aircraft control, *see* altimeter, automatic pilot, avionics,
Decca Navigation System, gyroscope, Inertial Navigation System, Instrument Landing System, radar, radio beam, transponder
Airline Companies, 210, 238
airmail service, 190, 198, 207-8, 237; in science fiction, 191-2
airplane(s): *see* heavier-than-aircraft; accidents, 183, 198-9, 207-8, 236-7, 239-40, 252-4; in science fiction, 114-9, 128-33, 191-5, 263-4; military use of, 163-4, 179-80, 183, 186, 193, 199, 200, 218, 221-2, 232, 235, 254-8; World War I, 201-4; World War II, 222-31; races and meets, 188, 221
airports, 174, 198, 239-9, 240
Albatross (Le Bris), 76-7, 78; Verne's creation, 117-9, 132
Alcock, John, 206
altimeter, 214-5

269

STRANGE GIRL

Also by Christopher Pike

THE THIRST SERIES

Remember Me

The Secret of Ka

Until the End

Bound to You

Chain Letter

WITCH WORLD, VOL. 1: *Red Queen*

WITCH WORLD, VOL. 2: *Black Knight*

STRANGE
GIRL

CHRISTOPHER PIKE

Simon Pulse

NEW YORK   LONDON   TORONTO   SYDNEY   NEW DELHI

SIMON PULSE

An imprint of Simon & Schuster Children's Publishing Division
1230 Avenue of the Americas, New York, New York 10020
This Simon Pulse edition November 2015
Text copyright © 2015 by Christopher Pike
Cover photograph copyright © 2015 by Ebru Sidar/Trevillion Images
All rights reserved, including the right of reproduction in whole or in part in any form.
SIMON PULSE and colophon are registered trademarks of Simon & Schuster, Inc.
For information about special discounts for bulk purchases, please contact
Simon & Schuster Special Sales at 1-866-506-1949 or business@simonandschuster.com.
The Simon & Schuster Speakers Bureau can bring authors to your live event. For more
information or to book an event contact the Simon & Schuster Speakers Bureau at
1-866-248-3049 or visit our website at www.simonspeakers.com.
Cover designed by Regina Flath
Interior designed by Hilary Zarycky
The text of this book was set in Adobe Garamond Pro.
Manufactured in the United States of America
2 4 6 8 10 9 7 5 3 1
The Library of Congress has cataloged the paperback edition as follows:
Pike, Christopher, 1955–, author.
Strange girl / by Christopher Pike. — First Simon Pulse paperback edition.
p. cm.
Summary: Told from the perspective of a seventeen-year-old boy in love with a mysterious
girl who seems to have an unearthly ability to heal, but the ability carries quite a cost.
[1. Love—Fiction. 2. Supernatural—Fiction. 3. Healers—Fiction. 4. Goddesses—Fiction.]
I. Title.
PZ7.P626St 2015   [Fic]—dc23   2015012476
ISBN 978-1-4814-5059-1 (hc)
ISBN 978-1-4814-5058-4 (pbk)
ISBN 978-1-4814-5060-7 (eBook)